COMPLETE

MathSmart®

Contents

Level 1 – Basic Skills

Level 2 – Further Your Understanding

Level 3 – Applications

Dear Parent or Guardian,

Thank you for choosing our book to help sharpen your child's math skills. Our primary goal is to provide a learning experience that is both fun and rewarding. This aim has guided the development of the series in a few key ways.

Our *Complete MathSmart* series has been designed to help children achieve mathematical excellence. Each grade has 3 levels. In level 1, your child learns all the basic math concepts necessary for success in his or her grade. Key concepts are accompanied by helpful three-part introductions: "Read This" explains the concept, "Example" demonstrates the concept, and "Try It" lets your child put the concept to use. In level 2, and to a greater extent in level 3, these concepts are worked into relatable problem-solving questions. These offer a greater challenge and point children to the every-day usefulness of math skills.

Fun activities, lively illustrations, and real-world scenarios throughout the book help bring the concepts to life and engage your child. Additionally, the QR codes in the book link to motion graphics that explain key ideas in a fun and active way. After your child has completed the core content, they will find two assessment tests. These will test your child's general ability to apply the concepts learned, and prepare them for standardized testing. Finally, your child can use the answer key in the back of the book to improve by comparing his or her results and methods.

With the help of these features, we hope to provide an enriching learning experience for your child. We would love to hear your feedback, and encourage you to share any stories of how *Complete MathSmart* has helped your child improve his or her math skills and gain confidence in the classroom.

Your Partner in Education,
Popular Book Company (Canada) Limited

LEVEL 1
BASIC SKILLS

1 Whole Numbers

• writing and comparing whole numbers to 100 000

 This   **Numbers can be expressed in different ways.**

Example   Write the number 58 237 in different ways.

Using a place value chart:

Thousands					
H	T	O	H	T	O
	5	8	2	3	7

In standard form: 58 237

In expanded form:

50 000 + 8000 + 200 + 30 + 7

In written form:

fifty-eight thousand two hundred thirty-seven

Remember to leave a space between the hundreds and the thousands digits.

Try It

Write the number below in expanded form and in words.

Thousands					
H	T	O	H	T	O
	2	5	0	7	9

In expanded form:

_____

In written form:

_____

Write the numbers.

① | **Standard Form** |
   |---|
   | 35 563 |

   Expanded form: _____

   Written form: _____

② | **Standard Form** |
   |---|
   | 90 921 |

   Expanded form: _____

   Written form: _____

③ | **Standard Form** |
   |---|
   | |

   Expanded form: 40 000 + 6000 + 200 + 10 + 4

   Written form: _____

④ | **Standard Form** |
   |---|
   | |

   Expanded form: _____

   Written form: seventy thousand six hundred twenty-nine

⑤ | **Standard Form** |
   |---|
   | |

   Expanded form: 80 000 + 4000 + 10

   Written form: _____

Write the value of each digit in bold.

⑥ 16 0**1**4 _____

⑦ 4**4** 842 _____

⑧ 6**6** 112 _____

⑨ 84 **3**13 _____

⑩ 57 14**2** _____

⑪ **9**4 218 _____

⑫ **2**6 607 _____

⑬ 27 06**2** _____

⑭ 89 **0**00 _____

⑮ 76 5**8**4 _____

Follow the arrows to read the 5-digit numbers displayed on the grid. Write them in standard form. Then fill in the blanks.

⑯

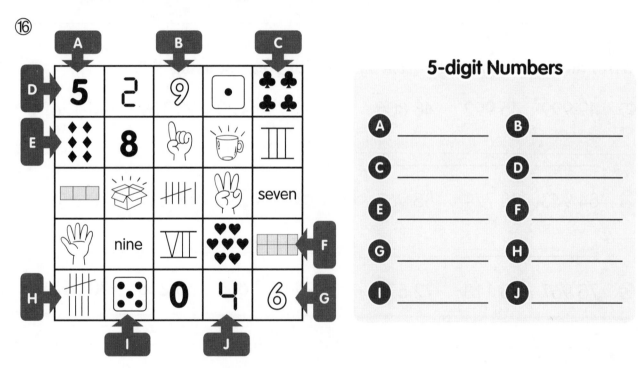

5-digit Numbers

Ⓐ _____ Ⓑ _____

Ⓒ _____ Ⓓ _____

Ⓔ _____ Ⓕ _____

Ⓖ _____ Ⓗ _____

Ⓘ _____ Ⓙ _____

⑰ A and _____ have the same digit in the ones place.

⑱ C and F have the same digit in the _____ place.

⑲ E and _____ have the same digit in the tens place.

⑳ C and H have the same digit in the _____ place.

㉑ _____ and _____ have the same digit in the thousands place.

Compare the pair of numbers in each place value chart. Then fill in the blanks with the numbers.

㉒

Thousands					
H	T	O	H	T	O
	8	5	2	0	0
	8	2	5	2	2

_____ < _____

㉓

Thousands					
H	T	O	H	T	O
	9	7	1	0	9
	9	7	9	4	5

_____ > _____

㉔

Thousands					
H	T	O	H	T	O
	6	8	2	9	3
	6	8	3	2	9

_____ > _____

㉕

Thousands					
H	T	O	H	T	O
	4	8	3	4	1
	4	3	8	7	6

_____ < _____

Write the numbers in order from smallest to greatest using "<".

㉖ 49 999   45 992   48 806

_____

㉗ 94 120   93 159   94 126

_____

㉘ 84 943   88 779   85 967

_____

㉙ 19 586   18 837   18 656

_____

㉚ 75 967   75 113   72 578

_____

㉛ 30 606   30 278   30 355

_____

㉜

$33 454 $35 255 $34 513 $34 202 $35 314

_____

Round each number to the nearest ten thousand.

③③ 52 417 _____

③④ 18 609 _____

③⑤ 22 735 _____

③⑥ 42 009 _____

③⑦ 84 328 _____

Hints

To round a number to the nearest ten thousand:

❶ Identify the digit in the thousands place.

❷ If it is 5 or greater, round the number up; otherwise, round it down.

e.g. 3**6** 482 ⟶ 40 000

6 > 5; round up

Complete the table by rounding each number to the nearest given place value.

③⑧

	ten thousands	thousands	hundreds	tens
43 509				
76 168				
52 945				
13 999				
24 547				

Use the given digits to form a number that fits each description.

③⑨

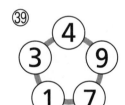

a. the smallest possible 5-digit number _____

b. the greatest possible 5-digit number _____

c. a number between 30 000 and 40 000 _____

④⓪

a. a number between 12 360 and 13 300 _____

b. a number that becomes 12 500 when rounded to the nearest hundred _____

c. the smallest number that becomes 53 000 when rounded to the nearest thousand _____

2 Multiplying and Dividing Whole Numbers

• multiplying 2-digit numbers and dividing 3-digit numbers

Read This

To multiply 2-digit numbers, multiply the top number first by the bottom number's ones digit, and then by its tens digit. Add the products to find the answer.

Example 29 x 64 = ?

```
  2 9           2 9
x 6 4    →    x 6 4
-------       -------
  1 1 6         1 1 6      Add "0" as a
                           placeholder.
29 x 4 = 116  1 7 4 0  ← 29 x 6 = 174
              -------
              1 8 5 6  ← 116 + 1740 = 1856
```

29 x 64 = [1856]

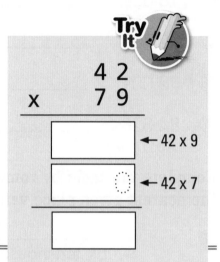

```
    4 2
x   7 9
---------
[        ]  ← 42 x 9
[        ]  ← 42 x 7
---------
[        ]
=
```

Do the multiplication.

①
```
    8 4
x   3 4
```

②
```
    6 8
x   4 2
```

③
```
    1 5
x   8 9
```

④
```
    4 5
x   3 7
```

⑤
```
    7 1
x   6 2
```

⑥
```
    3 9
x   5 4
```

⑦
```
    8 3
x   2 4
```

⑧
```
    5 7
x   1 6
```

⑨
```
    2 8
x   2 8
```

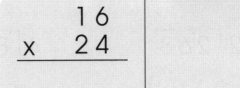
Do the multiplication. Show your work.

⑩ 16 x 24 = _____

⑪ 21 x 35 = _____

⑫ 43 x 28 = _____

⑬ 12 x 53 = _____

⑭ 29 x 62 = _____

⑮ 32 x 47 = _____

```
      1 6
x     2 4
```

Don't forget to align the numbers to the right and add "0" as a placeholder wherever needed.

Find the product of each pair of numbers. Then estimate to determine whether your answer is reasonable.

⑯ **39   72**

```
      3 9
x     7 2
```

Estimate:

_____ x _____ = _____

⑰ **28   91**

Estimate:

_____ x _____ = _____

Tips

To estimate a product, round the numbers to the nearest ten. Then multiply the rounded numbers.

Do the division.

⑱
$$2\overline{)268}$$

⑲
$$4\overline{)852}$$

Tips The steps for dividing 3-digit numbers are the same as the steps for dividing 2-digit numbers.

e.g.
$$\begin{array}{r} 2\,1\,5 \\ 3\overline{)6\,4\,5} \\ \underline{6} \\ 4 \\ \underline{3} \\ 1\,5 \\ \underline{1\,5} \end{array}$$

⑳
$$5\overline{)940}$$

㉑
$$3\overline{)936}$$

Do the division with remainders. Show your work.

㉒
$$4\overline{)173}$$

㉓
$$6\overline{)616}$$

Tips Add "0" as a placeholder when needed.

e.g.
placeholder
$$\begin{array}{r} 1\,0\,3\;R4 \\ 7\overline{)7\,2\,5} \\ \underline{7} \\ 2\,5 \\ \underline{2\,1} \\ 4 \end{array}$$

㉔
$$2\overline{)683}$$

㉕
$$8\overline{)525}$$

㉖
$$7\overline{)404}$$

Do the division. Show your work.

㉗

A 218 ÷ 3 = _____

B 497 ÷ 7 = _____

C 124 ÷ 8 = _____

D 874 ÷ 4 = _____

E 472 ÷ 3 = _____

F 500 ÷ 6 = _____

G 695 ÷ 7 = _____

H 837 ÷ 5 = _____

A

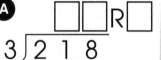

B

$$7\overline{)497}$$

C

D

E

F

G

H

Write the answers to complete the puzzle.

㉘

Across

A: 7 x 30

B: 208 ÷ 4

C: 270 ÷ 9

D: 30 x 69

E: 40 ÷ 10

F: 10 x 75

Down

A: 225 ÷ 9

C: 5 x 75

E: 322 ÷ 7

F: 19 x 4

G: 366 ÷ 3

3 Decimals

• writing, comparing, and representing decimals to hundredths

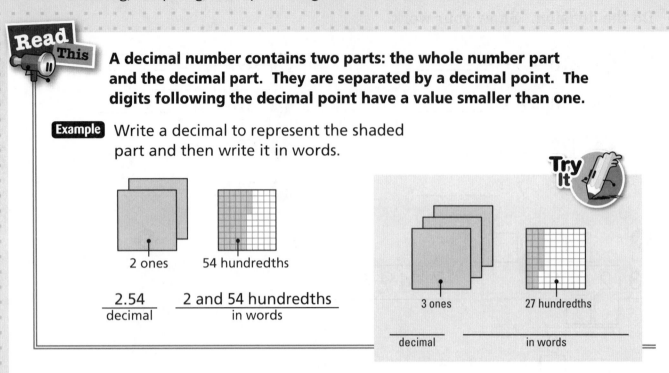

Read This

A decimal number contains two parts: the whole number part and the decimal part. They are separated by a decimal point. The digits following the decimal point have a value smaller than one.

Example Write a decimal to represent the shaded part and then write it in words.

2 ones   54 hundredths

$\underset{\text{decimal}}{2.54}$ $\underset{\text{in words}}{\underline{\text{2 and 54 hundredths}}}$

Try It

3 ones   27 hundredths

decimal   in words

Write a decimal to represent the shaded part of each diagram. Then write it in words.

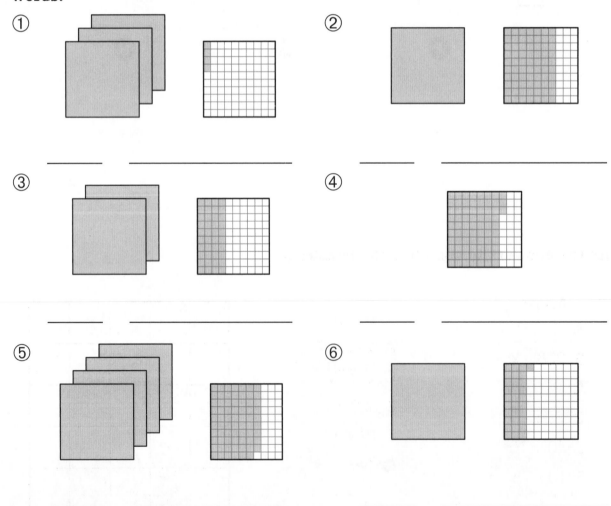

① _____ _____

② _____ _____

③ _____ _____

④ _____ _____

⑤ _____ _____

⑥ _____ _____

Draw a diagram to represent each decimal.

⑦ 1.56

⑧ 2.77

⑨ 1.08

⑩ 3.02

Write the value of each digit in bold.

⑪ 0.**5**1 _____

⑫ 2.4**7** _____

⑬ **2**3.46 _____

⑭ 1**3**.21 _____

⑮ 0.2**6** _____

⑯ 47.3**1** _____

⑰ 5.0**9** _____

⑱ 16.**7**2 _____

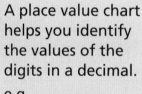

A place value chart helps you identify the values of the digits in a decimal.
e.g.

Ones	Tenths	Hundredths
3	4	6

↑ means 0.4   ↑ means 0.06

Circle the equivalent decimals in each group.

⑲ 1.2
1.02
1.20

⑳ 3.01
3.10
3.1

㉑ 0.8
0.18
0.80

㉒ 2.50
2.55
2.5

㉓ 4.0
4.10
4.00

㉔ 2.00
2
20.0

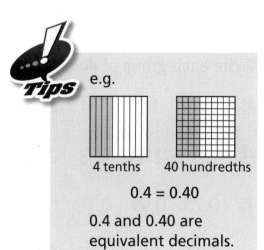

e.g.

4 tenths   40 hundredths

0.4 = 0.40

0.4 and 0.40 are equivalent decimals.

Compare the decimals. Write ">" or "<" in the circles.

㉕ 3.22 ◯ 3.25   ㉖ 1.80 ◯ 1.08   ㉗ 4.90 ◯ 4.09

㉘ 2.87 ◯ 1.87   ㉙ 3.48 ◯ 4.38   ㉚ 2.46 ◯ 2.4

㉛ 2.99 ◯ 3.01   ㉜ 7.12 ◯ 7.02   ㉝ 1.25 ◯ 1.50

㉞ 8.68 ◯ 8.8   ㉟ 6.85 ◯ 5.68   ㊱ 3.00 ◯ 3.03

㊲ 4.50 ◯ 4.05   ㊳ 4.41 ◯ 4.14   ㊴ 0.75 ◯ 7.5

Locate each group of decimals on the number line. Then write them in order from smallest to greatest.

㊵ 0.2 0.15 0.24 0.3

_____

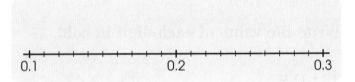

㊶ 0.75 0.6 0.65 0.9

_____

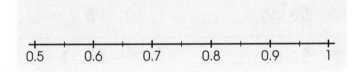

㊷ 0.82 0.78 0.8 0.88

_____

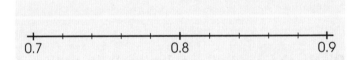

Write each group of decimals in order.

㊸ 1.45 1.5 1.4 1.54   _____ < _____ < _____ < _____

㊹ 2.9 2.09 3.2 2.93   _____ > _____ > _____ > _____

㊺ 0.73 0.97 0.79 0.39   _____ < _____ < _____ < _____

㊻ 5.15 5.5 5.05 5.51   _____ > _____ > _____ > _____

Locate each number on the number line. Then round it to the nearest tenth.

㊼ 2.12 ➡ _____　　㊽ 3.07 ➡ _____　　㊾ 0.39 ➡ _____

```
+--+--+--+--+--+--+--+--+--+--+        +--+--+--+--+--+--+--+--+--+--+        +--+--+--+--+--+--+--+--+--+--+
2.1                    2.2            3                     3.1            0.3                    0.4
```

㊿ 5.27 ➡ _____　　51 4.39 ➡ _____　　52 12.14 ➡ _____

```
+--+--+--+--+--+--+--+--+--+--+        +--+--+--+--+--+--+--+--+--+--+        +--+--+--+--+--+--+--+--+--+--+
5.2                    5.3            4.3                   4.4            12.1                   12.2
```

Round the decimals. Complete the table.

53

	Round to the nearest	
	one	tenth
1.64		
2.43		
5.09		
3.77		
0.92		

To round a decimal to the nearest tenth, check the digit in its hundredths place.

e.g.

5.63 —round down→ 5.6

3 < 5; round down

5.68 —round up→ 5.7

8 > 5; round up

Write a decimal that fits each description.

54 a decimal that is greater than 2.54 but smaller than 2.63 _____

55 a decimal that has 3 in its hundredths place and is between 4 and 5 _____

56 a decimal that is rounded to 5.1 when rounded to the nearest tenth _____

4 Adding Decimals

- adding decimals to hundredths

Align the decimal points when adding decimals. Write "0" as a placeholder when necessary.

Example 7.23 + 5.9 = ?

Align the decimal points.

```
  7.23
+ 5.90
```
placeholder

Add as if they are whole numbers.

```
  7.23
+ 5.90
  13 13
```

Add the decimal point to the answer.

```
  7.23
+ 5.90
  13.13
```

7.23 + 5.9 = **13.13**

Try It

```
  3.01
+ 2.78
```

Do the addition.

①
```
  0.7
+ 0.8
```

②
```
  1.93
+ 8.75
```

③
```
  3.20
+ 6.62
```

④
```
  3.41
+ 4.60
```

⑤
```
  10.23
+  2.70
```

⑥
```
   0.99
+ 12.88
```

⑦
```
  20.93
+  7.28
```

⑧
```
   6.54
+ 27.69
```

⑨
```
  27.84
+  3.07
```

⑩
```
  30.30
+  6.84
```

⑪
```
   5.83
+ 23.00
```

⑫
```
  49.01
+  9.09
```

⑬
```
   5.50
+ 50.90
```

⑭
```
  24.78
+  1.22
```

⑮
```
  23.45
+ 34.56
```

⑯
```
  13.59
+ 12.64
```

Do the addition. Show your work.

⑰ 5.14 + 7.82 = _____

⑱ 6.91 + 0.78 = _____

⑲ 2.73 + 4.9   = _____

⑳ 7 + 1.23   = _____

㉑ 5.9 + 8.73   = _____

㉒ 7.03 + 2.9   = _____

㉓ 11.67 + 40.9 = _____

㉔ 22.45 + 6.7 = _____

㉕ 52.93 + 9.2 = _____

㉖ 89 + 2.82   = _____

㉗ 41.05 + 26.4 = _____

㉘ 17.42 + 35   = _____

$$\begin{array}{r} 5.14 \\ +\ 7.82 \\ \hline \end{array}$$

Match each pair of decimals with its sum.

㉙

2.09	12.47	•
7.63	7.02	•
8.24	8.3	•
9.88	5.76	•
9.22	6.24	•

Sum

• 16.54
• 14.56
• 15.64
• 14.65
• 15.46

Estimate each answer. Then add.

㉚
```
  9.32
+ 0.95
```
Estimate
9
+ 1

㉛
```
  9.85
+ 1.32
```
Estimate

㉜
```
  5.23
+ 6.09
```
Estimate

㉝
```
  10.93
+  0.21
```
Estimate

㉞
```
  70.94
   3.50
+ 11.39
```
Estimate

㉟
```
  29.84
  39.99
+  5.17
```
Estimate

Find the totals.

㊱  **$19.99**

$25.45

_____

㊲  **1.7 L**

0.88 L

_____

㊳  **3.75 kg**

2.05 kg

_____

㊴ **0.32 GB**

 1.09 GB

_____

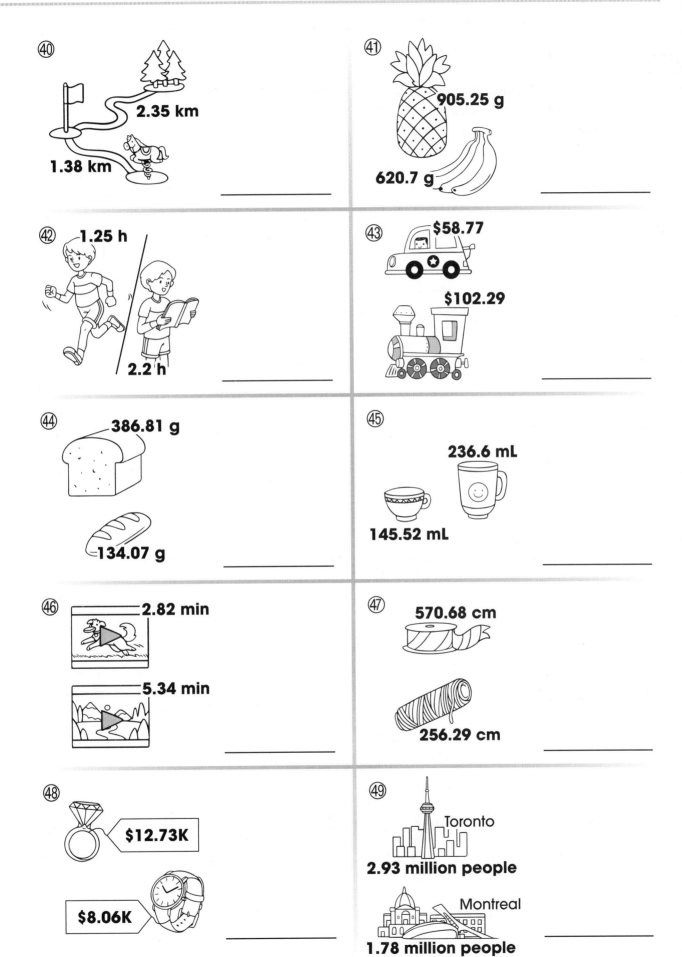

㊵ 2.35 km

1.38 km

_____

㊶ 905.25 g

620.7 g

_____

㊷ 1.25 h

2.2 h

_____

㊸ $58.77

$102.29

_____

㊹ 386.81 g

134.07 g

_____

㊺ 236.6 mL

145.52 mL

_____

㊻ 2.82 min

5.34 min

_____

㊼ 570.68 cm

256.29 cm

_____

㊽ $12.73K

$8.06K

_____

㊾ Toronto

2.93 million people

Montreal

1.78 million people

_____

5 Subtracting Decimals

- subtracting decimals to hundredths

Read This

Align the decimal points when subtracting decimals. Add "0" as a placeholder when necessary.

Example 9.43 – 7.86 = ?

Align the decimal points.

$$\begin{array}{r} 9.43 \\ -\ 7.86 \\ \hline \end{array}$$

➡

Subtract as if they are whole numbers.

$$\begin{array}{r} 9.43 \\ -\ 7.86 \\ \hline 1\ 57 \end{array}$$

➡

Add the decimal point to the answer.

$$\begin{array}{r} 9.43 \\ -\ 7.86 \\ \hline 1.57 \end{array}$$

9.43 – 7.86 = ☐ 1.57

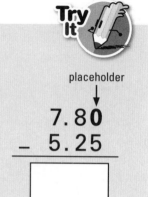

Try It

placeholder
↓

$$\begin{array}{r} 7.8\mathbf{0} \\ -\ 5.25 \\ \hline \end{array}$$

Do the subtraction.

①
$$\begin{array}{r} 0.7 \\ -\ 0.2 \\ \hline \end{array}$$

②
$$\begin{array}{r} 8.3 \\ -\ 1.8 \\ \hline \end{array}$$

③
$$\begin{array}{r} 9.20 \\ -\ 2.91 \\ \hline \end{array}$$

④
$$\begin{array}{r} 5.00 \\ -\ 3.82 \\ \hline \end{array}$$

⑤
$$\begin{array}{r} 15.34 \\ -\ 6.90 \\ \hline \end{array}$$

⑥
$$\begin{array}{r} 12.40 \\ -\ 8.62 \\ \hline \end{array}$$

⑦
$$\begin{array}{r} 17.04 \\ -\ 12.00 \\ \hline \end{array}$$

⑧
$$\begin{array}{r} 9.57 \\ -\ 0.88 \\ \hline \end{array}$$

⑨
$$\begin{array}{r} 8.04 \\ -\ 4.98 \\ \hline \end{array}$$

⑩
$$\begin{array}{r} 20.23 \\ -\ 5.07 \\ \hline \end{array}$$

⑪
$$\begin{array}{r} 32.16 \\ -\ 8.45 \\ \hline \end{array}$$

⑫
$$\begin{array}{r} 50.00 \\ -\ 4.85 \\ \hline \end{array}$$

⑬
$$\begin{array}{r} 12.83 \\ -\ 8.95 \\ \hline \end{array}$$

⑭
$$\begin{array}{r} 15.00 \\ -\ 13.07 \\ \hline \end{array}$$

⑮
$$\begin{array}{r} 26.19 \\ -\ 17.43 \\ \hline \end{array}$$

⑯
$$\begin{array}{r} 43.08 \\ -\ 29.79 \\ \hline \end{array}$$

Do the subtraction.

⑰ $2 - 0.02$ = _____

⑱ $9.03 - 4$ = _____

⑲ $7.9 - 4.13$ = _____

⑳ $10.4 - 2.13$ = _____

㉑ $8.1 - 5.08$ = _____

㉒ $15 - 3.62$ = _____

㉓ $12.1 - 4.23$ = _____

㉔ $9.5 - 7.68$ = _____

㉕ $0.96 - 0.08$ = _____

㉖ $0.72 - 0.5$ = _____

㉗ $1.1 - 0.84$ = _____

㉘ $2.3 - 1.49$ = _____

㉙ $2.6 - 0.26$ = _____

㉚ $0.36 - 0.3$ = _____

㉛ $42.1 - 9.63$ = _____

㉜ $38 - 11.62$ = _____

㉝ $36.37 - 15.6$ = _____

㉞ $38.9 - 26.85$ = _____

㉟ $42.48 - 22.7$ = _____

㊱ $12.2 - 10.61$ = _____

Do your work here.

$\frac{1}{2} = 0.5$

$2 =$

Do the subtraction and colour the boxes containing the answers in the chart.

㊲ 9.2 – 7.8 = ________

㊳ 9.3 – 1.3 = ________

㊴ 9.23 – 5.87 = ________

㊵ 8.2 – 5.8 = ________

㊶ 7.2 – 5.2 = ________

㊷ 3 – 0.39 = ________

㊸ 5 – 0.8 = ________

㊹ 5.2 – 3.97 = ________

㊺ 7.9 – 7.25 = ________

㊻ 15 – 7.3 = ________

㊼ 9.37 – 1.99 = ________

㊽ 8.06 – 5.61 = ________

㊾ 16.75 – 9.26 = ________

㊿ 12.13 – 2.67 = ________

2.19	5.07	3.36		
5.4	2	1.23		
1.01	4.01	7.38	5	3.68
0.87	5	4.2	0.9	3
4.8	6.28	8	6.5	1.21
2.22	3.13	0.65	4.97	0.29
3.6	1.88	2.4	3.46	8.7
0.7	5.9	7.7	0.61	10
7.49	9.46	1.4	2.61	2.45

Write the number formed by the coloured boxes on the badge.

Estimate each answer. Then do the subtraction.

(51)
$$
\begin{array}{r}
14.49 \\
-\ \ 9.32 \\
\hline
\end{array}
$$
Estimate
$\begin{array}{r} 14 \\ -\ \ 9 \\ \hline \end{array}$

(52)
$$
\begin{array}{r}
26.67 \\
-\ 18.91 \\
\hline
\end{array}
$$
Estimate

(53)
$$
\begin{array}{r}
33.48 \\
-\ 27.75 \\
\hline
\end{array}
$$
Estimate

(54)
$$
\begin{array}{r}
80.95 \\
-\ 62.08 \\
\hline
\end{array}
$$
Estimate

(55)
$$
\begin{array}{r}
21.35 \\
-\ 19.73 \\
\hline
\end{array}
$$
Estimate

(56)
$$
\begin{array}{r}
54.99 \\
-\ 16.58 \\
\hline
\end{array}
$$
Estimate

Find the differences.

(57)

850 mL

236.6 mL

(58)

$360.88

$199.99

(59)

28.36 km

21.87 km

(60)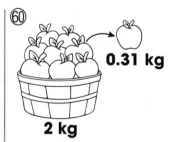

0.31 kg

2 kg

6 Multiplying Decimals

- multiplying decimals by 10, 100, or 1000

Read This

When multiplying a decimal by 10, 100, or 1000, move the decimal point 1, 2, or 3 places to the right respectively.

Example Do the multiplication.

Move the decimal point to the right.

1.75 x 10 = 17.5
1 place   1 zero

1.75 x 100 = 175
2 places   2 zeros

1.75 x 1000 = 1750
3 places   3 zeros

4.32 x 10 = ☐
1 place

4.32 x 100 = ☐
2 places

4.32 x 1000 = ☐
3 places

Do the multiplication.

① 0.4 x 10   = _____

   0.4 x 100   = _____

   0.4 x 1000 = _____

② 0.02 x 10   = _____

   0.02 x 100   = _____

   0.02 x 1000 = _____

③ 0.12 x 10   = _____

   0.12 x 100   = _____

   0.12 x 1000 = _____

④ 3.9 x 10   = _____

   3.9 x 100   = _____

   3.9 x 1000   = _____

⑤ 2.5 x 10   = _____

   2.5 x 100   = _____

   2.5 x 1000   = _____

⑥ 1.04 x 10   = _____

   1.04 x 100   = _____

   1.04 x 1000 = _____

⑦ 6.39 x 10   = _____

   6.39 x 100   = _____

   6.39 x 1000 = _____

⑧ 7.42 x 10   = _____

   7.42 x 100   = _____

   7.42 x 1000 = _____

Find the totals.

⑨  10 lollipops: _____

$0.26

⑩  100 cookies: _____

$0.51

⑪  1000 chocolates: _____

51.2 g

⑫  10 eggs: _____

43.2 g

⑬  100 bottles: _____

0.75 L

⑭  10 juice boxes: _____

198.5 mL

⑮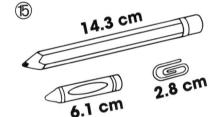

a. 1000 paper clips: _____

b. 100 crayons: _____

c. 10 pencils: _____

14.3 cm **6.1 cm** **2.8 cm**

⑯

a. 1000 marbles: _____

b. 100 baseballs: _____

c. 10 basketballs: _____

$0.16 **$2.50** **$38.12**

⑰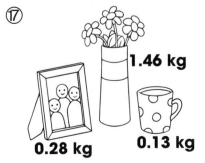

a. 100 vases: _____

b. 10 picture frames: _____

c. 1000 mugs: _____

1.46 kg **0.28 kg** **0.13 kg**

Solve.

⑱ 4.6   ⟶   _____
5.21   **x 10**   _____
3.09   _____

㉑ _____   ⟶   3.2
_____   **x 10**   5.8
_____   10.7

⑲ 1.28   _____
0.07   **x 100**   _____
6.41   _____

㉒ _____   3
_____   **x 100**   40
_____   210

⑳ 0.3   _____
1.46   **x 1000**   _____
8.01   _____

㉓ _____   70
_____   **x 1000**   810
_____   90

Fill in the blanks with 10, 100, or 1000.

㉔

Count the number of decimal places you move the decimal point to help find the answer.

a.

$3.6 \times$ _____ $= 36$
1

$0.25 \times$ _____ $= 25$
1 2

$1.06 \times$ _____ $= 10.6$
1

$3.69 \times$ _____ $= 3690$
1 2 3

b. _____ $\times 0.48 = 4.8$

c. _____ $\times 0.05 = 50$

d. $2.04 \times$ _____ $= 20.4$

e. $8.6 \times$ _____ $= 86$

f. _____ $\times 5.7 = 5700$

g. $2.3 \times$ _____ $= 2300$

Show your steps and solve. Multiply the numbers in a different order if needed.

㉕   0.6 x 5 x 2

   = 0.6 x _____

   = _____

㉖   5 x 1.8 x 2

   = 5 x _____ x _____

   = _____ x _____

   = _____

Hints

Commutative Property of Multiplication

Numbers can be multiplied in any order without affecting the product.

Rearranging numbers can help you find friendly numbers to make multiplying easier.

e.g.   2 x 0.8 x 5
     = 2 x 5 x 0.8 ◄— rearranged
     = 10 x 0.8 ◄— got 10, a friendly
     = 8   number

㉗   2 x 3.86 x 5

㉘   1.77 x 4 x 25

㉙   20 x 6.14 x 5

㉚   50 x 0.49 x 2

㉛   10 x 0.82 x 10

㉜   200 x 1.99 x 5

㉝   26.3 x 8 x 125

Solve. Time yourself.

㉞   5 x 8.2 x 2   = _____

㉟   5 x 39.27 x 200 = _____

㊱   0.23 x 4 x 25   = _____

㊲   4 x 25 x 5.63   = _____

㊳   50 x 1.22 x 20   = _____

㊴   250 x 4 x 18.05 = _____

Use the commutative property of multiplication to help find the answers quickly.

Time:

_____ min

㊵   5 x 16.2 x 2   = _____

㊶   125 x 6.5 x 8 = _____

7 Dividing Decimals

- dividing decimals by 10, 100, or 1000

Read This

When dividing a decimal by 10, 100, or 1000, move the decimal point 1, 2, or 3 places to the left respectively.

Example Do the division.

Move the decimal point to the left.

$5.72 \div 10 = \underline{0.572}$
1 place   1 zero

$5.72 \div 100 = \underline{0.0572}$
2 places   2 zeros

$5.72 \div 1000 = \underline{0.00572}$
3 places   3 zeros

Try It

$6.23 \div 10 = \underline{\hspace{2cm}}$
1 place

$6.23 \div 100 = \underline{\hspace{2cm}}$
2 places

$6.23 \div 1000 = \underline{\hspace{2cm}}$
3 places

Do the division.

① a. $98 \div 10 = \underline{\hspace{2cm}}$

   b. $98 \div 100 = \underline{\hspace{2cm}}$

   c. $98 \div 1000 = \underline{\hspace{2cm}}$

② a. $5 \div 10 = \underline{\hspace{2cm}}$

   b. $5 \div 100 = \underline{\hspace{2cm}}$

   c. $5 \div 1000 = \underline{\hspace{2cm}}$

③ a. $0.7 \div 10 = \underline{\hspace{2cm}}$

   b. $0.7 \div 100 = \underline{\hspace{2cm}}$

   c. $0.7 \div 1000 = \underline{\hspace{2cm}}$

④ a. $2.05 \div 10 = \underline{\hspace{2cm}}$

   b. $2.05 \div 100 = \underline{\hspace{2cm}}$

   c. $2.05 \div 1000 = \underline{\hspace{2cm}}$

⑤ $2.8 \div 10 = \underline{\hspace{2cm}}$

⑥ $3.16 \div 10 = \underline{\hspace{2cm}}$

⑦ $1.4 \div 100 = \underline{\hspace{2cm}}$

⑧ $4 \div 100 = \underline{\hspace{2cm}}$

⑨ $16 \div 100 = \underline{\hspace{2cm}}$

⑩ $8 \div 1000 = \underline{\hspace{2cm}}$

⑪ $3.1 \div 10 = \underline{\hspace{2cm}}$

⑫ $2.56 \div 1000 = \underline{\hspace{2cm}}$

⑬ $44 \div 1000 = \underline{\hspace{2cm}}$

⑭ $1.18 \div 100 = \underline{\hspace{2cm}}$

⑮ $0.9 \div 1000 = \underline{\hspace{2cm}}$

⑯ $9 \div 10 = \underline{\hspace{2cm}}$

⑰ $25 \div 10 = \underline{\hspace{2cm}}$

⑱ $0.92 \div 100 = \underline{\hspace{2cm}}$

Divide into equal groups.

⑲

a. 10 bags:

_____ ÷ 10

= _____ (kg)

b. 100 bags:

⑳

a. 100 sections:

b. 1000 sections:

㉑

a. 100 buckets:

b. 1000 buckets:

㉒

a. 10 days:

b. 100 days:

㉓

a. 10 pieces:

b. 100 pieces:

㉔

a. 10 bags:

b. 100 bags:

Help Sam check his answers. Put a check mark in the circle if the answer is correct; otherwise, put a cross and write the correct answer beside it.

㉕

Math Quiz

Name: _Sam_

1. $20.1 \div 10 =$ _2.1_ ◯

2. $399 \div 100 =$ _3.99_ ◯

3. $4500 \div 1000 =$ _0.45_ ◯

4. $825 \div 100 =$ _8.25_ ◯

5. $4.7 \div 10 =$ _0.47_ ◯

6. $250 \div 1000 =$ _2.05_ ◯

7. $36 \div 100 =$ _0.36_ ◯

8. $60.8 \div 10 =$ _6.08_ ◯

9. $13 \div 100 =$ _1.3_ ◯

10. $5020 \div 1000 =$ _5.02_ ◯

11. $1240 \div 1000 =$ _12.4_ ◯

12. $16.8 \div 100 =$ _1.68_ ◯

13. $40.5 \div 100 =$ _4.05_ ◯

14. $840 \div 10 =$ _84_ ◯

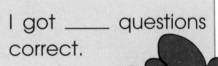

I got _____ questions correct.

Find the missing numbers.

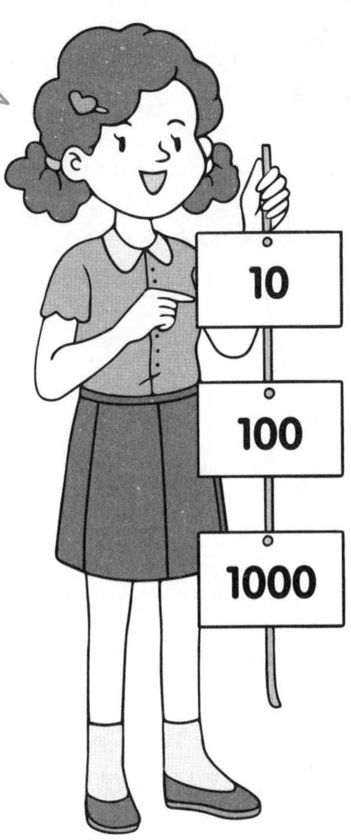
These are the possible answers.
10
100
1000

㉖ 2.6 ÷ ______ = 0.26

㉗ 47 ÷ ______ = 0.47

㉘ 1300 ÷ ______ = 1.3

㉙ 285 ÷ ______ = 2.85

㉚ 0.5 ÷ ______ = 0.05

㉛ 17 ÷ ______ = 0.17

㉜ 360 ÷ ______ = 3.6

㉝ 409 ÷ ______ = 4.09

㉞ 24 ÷ ______ = 0.24

㉟ 955 ÷ ______ = 95.5

㊱ 1250 ÷ ______ = 1.25

㊲ 4300 ÷ ______ = 4.3

㊳ 630 ÷ ______ = 63

㊴ 21 ÷ ______ = 0.021

For each answer, add the decimal point in the correct place.

Tips You might need to add "0" to make an answer correct.

㊵ 158 ÷ 10 = 158

㊶ 62 ÷ 10 = 6.2

㊷ 37 ÷ 100 = 37

㊸ 54 ÷ 10 = 0.54

㊹ 52 ÷ 1000 = 52

㊺ 168 ÷ 1000 = 1.68

㊻ 420 ÷ 100 = 42

㊼ 8 ÷ 10 = 0.08

㊽ 3200 ÷ 1000 = 32

㊾ 24 ÷ 100 = 24

㊿ 610 ÷ 10 = 61

(51) 9 ÷ 10 = 0.9

(52) 413 ÷ 100 = 0.413

(53) 302 ÷ 1000 = 302

(54) 6 ÷ 10 = 0.006

8 Fractions

- understanding and using fractions

A fraction contains a numerator (the number above the line) and a denominator (the number below the line).

Example Write fractions to represent the shaded parts of the diagrams.

$$\frac{1}{3}$$

$$\frac{3}{4}$$ ← numerator
← denominator

Try It

_____

_____

Write fractions for the shaded and unshaded parts of each diagram.

①   Shaded: _____

Unshaded: _____

②   Shaded: _____

Unshaded: _____

③ 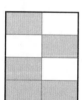 Shaded: _____

Unshaded: _____

④ 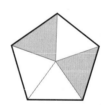 Shaded: _____

Unshaded: _____

⑤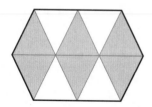

Shaded: _____

Unshaded: _____

⑥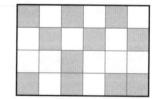

Shaded: _____

Unshaded: _____

Colour each diagram to show the fractions.

⑦

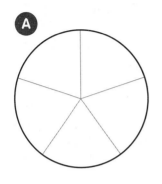

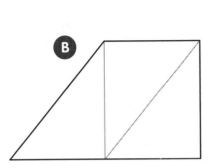

A	red: $\frac{2}{5}$; blue: $\frac{1}{5}$
B	yellow: $\frac{2}{3}$; green: $\frac{1}{3}$
C	blue: $\frac{4}{6}$; green: $\frac{2}{6}$
D	red: $\frac{3}{8}$; green: $\frac{1}{8}$
E	yellow: $\frac{3}{6}$; blue: $\frac{1}{6}$

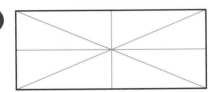

Complete the fractions for each set using the given denominator.

⑧

Shaded —
$\dfrac{}{5}$

Unshaded —
$\dfrac{}{5}$

⑨

Shaded —
$\dfrac{}{4}$

Unshaded —
$\dfrac{}{4}$

⑩

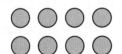

Shaded —
$\dfrac{}{6}$

Unshaded —
$\dfrac{}{6}$

⑪

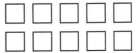

Shaded —
$\dfrac{}{3}$

Unshaded —
$\dfrac{}{3}$

Colour the correct number of shapes for each fraction.

⑫
$\frac{1}{4}$
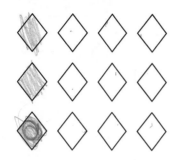

⑬
$\frac{2}{5}$
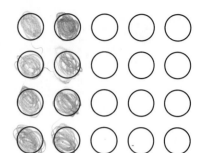

⑭
$\frac{5}{8}$

⑮
$\frac{7}{10}$
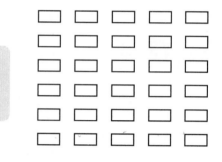

Check the correct answers.

⑯ Which diagrams show $\frac{2}{3}$ with their shaded parts?

Ⓐ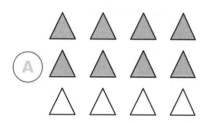

Ⓑ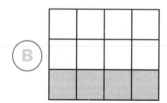

Ⓒ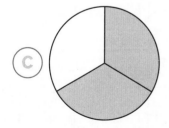

⑰ Which fractions represent the shaded part of the diagram?

Ⓐ $\frac{1}{3}$　Ⓑ $\frac{1}{4}$　Ⓒ $\frac{4}{12}$

⑱ A fraction represents the shaded part of the diagram. The denominator is 3. What is the numerator?

Ⓐ 1　Ⓑ 2　Ⓒ 3

Use the pictures to help find the answers.

⑲ 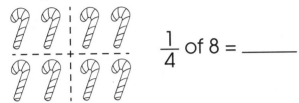 $\frac{1}{2}$ of 4 = _____

Divide the items into equal groups. Then count the number of parts.

e.g.

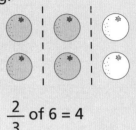

$\frac{2}{3}$ of 6 = 4

⑳ 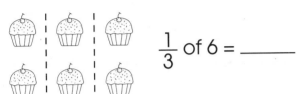 $\frac{1}{4}$ of 8 = _____

㉑  $\frac{1}{3}$ of 6 = _____

㉒

$\frac{2}{5}$ of 10 = _____

㉓

$\frac{3}{4}$ of 8 = _____

㉔

$\frac{1}{3}$ of 15 = _____

㉕

$\frac{2}{6}$ of 18 = _____

㉖

$\frac{5}{8}$ of 16 = _____

㉗

$\frac{2}{5}$ of 20 = _____

9 Ordering Fractions

• ordering fractions with the same denominator

To compare fractions with the same denominator, compare their numerators.

Example Compare $\frac{1}{3}$ and $\frac{2}{3}$.

$$\frac{1}{3} \quad \frac{2}{3} \quad \leftarrow 1 < 2$$
$$\leftarrow \text{same denominator}$$

$\frac{1}{3}$ is smaller than $\frac{2}{3}$.

Which fraction is greater? Circle it.

$$\frac{3}{4} \qquad \frac{1}{4}$$

Write the fraction that represents the shaded part of each diagram. Then circle the specified fraction in each pair.

① Circle the smaller fraction.

a.
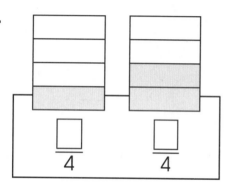

b.
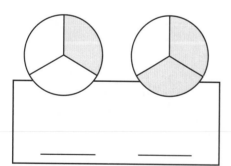

c.
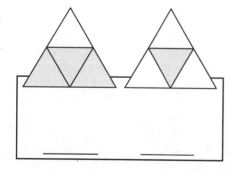

② Circle the greater fraction.

a.
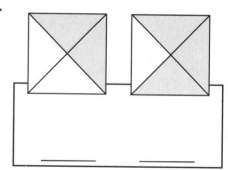

b.
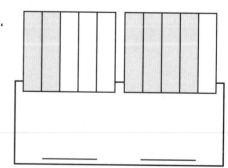

c.
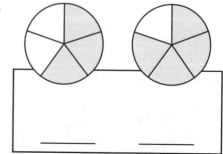

Complete the number lines. Then compare the fractions and write ">" or "<" in the circles.

③  $\frac{1}{3}\bigcirc\frac{2}{3}$

④ 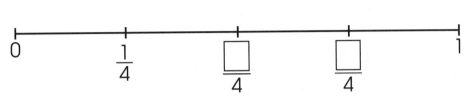 $\frac{3}{4}\bigcirc\frac{1}{4}$

⑤ 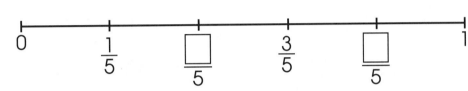 $\frac{3}{5}\bigcirc\frac{4}{5}$

⑥ 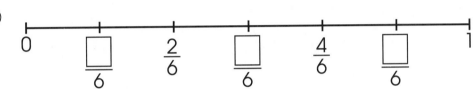 $\frac{2}{6}\bigcirc\frac{5}{6}$

⑦ 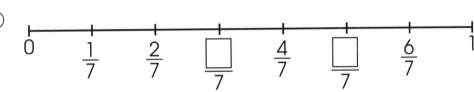 $\frac{5}{7}\bigcirc\frac{3}{7}$

Write the fractions in the specified order using ">" or "<".

⑧ From smallest to largest:

   a. $\frac{1}{8}$, $\frac{5}{8}$, $\frac{4}{8}$

   _____

   b. $\frac{2}{6}$, $\frac{5}{6}$, $\frac{1}{6}$

   _____

   c. $\frac{3}{7}$, $\frac{6}{7}$, $\frac{7}{7}$

   _____

⑨ From largest to smallest:

   a. $\frac{5}{10}$, $\frac{3}{10}$, $\frac{8}{10}$

   _____

   b. $\frac{7}{12}$, $\frac{10}{12}$, $\frac{8}{12}$

   _____

   c. $\frac{1}{9}$, $\frac{2}{9}$, $\frac{4}{9}$

   _____

Write fractions for the shaded parts of the diagrams. Then put the fractions in order.

⑩ **A** 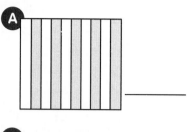 _____

B 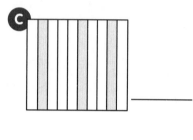 _____

C 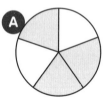 _____

_____ > _____ > _____

⑪ **A** 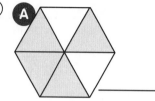 _____

B  _____

C _____

_____ < _____ < _____

⑫ **A** 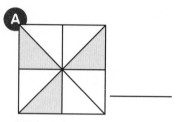 _____

B 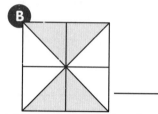 _____

C 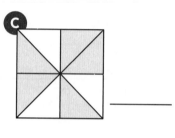 _____

_____ > _____ > _____

⑬ **A** _____   **B** _____   **C** _____

_____ < _____ < _____

Circle the fractions that fit each description.

⑭ smaller than $\frac{3}{5}$

$\frac{4}{5}$ $\frac{2}{5}$ $\frac{1}{5}$

⑮ greater than $\frac{4}{7}$

$\frac{5}{7}$ $\frac{3}{7}$ $\frac{6}{7}$

⑯ between $\frac{2}{8}$ and $\frac{7}{8}$

$\frac{5}{8}$ $\frac{1}{8}$ $\frac{6}{8}$

⑰ smaller than $\frac{2}{6}$ or greater than $\frac{4}{6}$

$\frac{5}{6}$ $\frac{3}{6}$ $\frac{1}{6}$

Colour each diagram to show a fraction that matches the description. Then write the fraction.

⑱ greater than $\frac{3}{5}$

⑲ smaller than $\frac{5}{8}$

⑳ smaller than $\frac{7}{10}$

㉑ greater than $\frac{5}{7}$

㉒ between $\frac{1}{6}$ and $\frac{5}{6}$

㉓ between $\frac{4}{9}$ and $\frac{7}{9}$

㉔ smaller than $\frac{4}{12}$

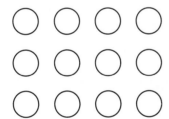

㉕ greater than $\frac{6}{11}$

㉖ between $\frac{5}{13}$ and $\frac{8}{13}$

㉗ between $\frac{8}{14}$ and $\frac{13}{14}$

10 Improper Fractions and Mixed Numbers

- using improper fractions and mixed numbers

There are three types of fractions.

- **Proper fraction:** the numerator is smaller than the denominator
- **Improper fraction:** the numerator is greater than, or equal to, the denominator
- **Mixed number:** formed by a whole number and a proper fraction

Example Name the fractions.

$\frac{3}{7}$ ___proper fraction___

$\frac{10}{7}$ ___improper fraction___

$1\frac{3}{7}$ ___mixed number___

Try It

$1\frac{1}{6}$ _____

$\frac{2}{5}$ _____

$\frac{3}{2}$ _____

**Sort the fractions into the correct categories.
Then answer the question.**

①

$\frac{2}{6}$ $\qquad$ $\frac{5}{7}$ $\qquad$ $\frac{5}{2}$

$1\frac{1}{2}$ $\qquad$ $3\frac{1}{4}$ $\qquad$ $2\frac{2}{3}$

$\frac{10}{12}$ $\qquad$ $\frac{1}{3}$ $\qquad$ $\frac{8}{8}$

$\frac{4}{3}$ $\qquad$ $\frac{9}{6}$ $\qquad$ $1\frac{1}{6}$

Proper Fraction

_____ _____ _____ _____

Improper Fraction

_____ _____ _____ _____

Mixed Number

_____ _____ _____ _____

Proper fractions, improper fractions, and mixed numbers are all fractions, but improper fractions and mixed numbers have something in common that proper fractions do not. What is it?

_____

_____

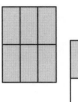
Write the shaded part of each diagram as an improper fraction and a mixed number.

②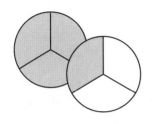

$\frac{\square}{3}$ $\square \frac{\square}{3}$

③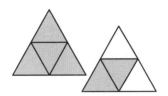

_____   _____

④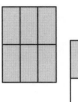

_____   _____

⑤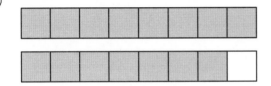

_____   _____

⑥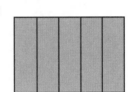

_____   _____

⑦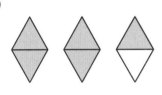

_____   _____

⑧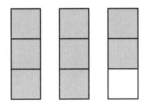

_____   _____

⑨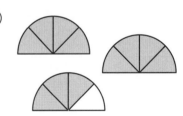

_____   _____

⑩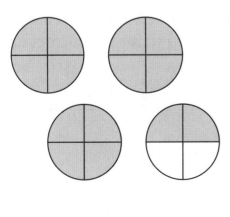

_____   _____

⑪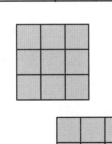

_____   _____

Convert the improper fractions into mixed numbers.

⑫ $\dfrac{9}{2} = $ _____

⑬ $\dfrac{15}{4} = $ _____

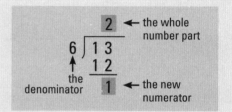
⑭ $\dfrac{17}{5} = $ _____

⑮ $\dfrac{10}{7} = $ _____

⑯ $\dfrac{8}{3} = $ _____

⑰ $\dfrac{9}{4} = $ _____

⑱ $\dfrac{12}{5} = $ _____

⑲ $\dfrac{11}{4} = $ _____

⑳ $\dfrac{16}{5} = $ _____

㉑ $\dfrac{19}{8} = $ _____

㉒ $\dfrac{17}{7} = $ _____

㉓ $\dfrac{10}{3} = $ _____

Check if the improper fractions were converted into mixed numbers correctly. If a conversion is incorrect, put a cross in the circle and write the correct answer.

㉔ $\dfrac{8}{5} = 1\dfrac{3}{5}$ ◯ _____

㉕ $\dfrac{7}{2} = 2\dfrac{3}{2}$ ◯ _____

㉖ $\dfrac{10}{3} = 3\dfrac{1}{3}$ ◯ _____

㉗ $\dfrac{14}{5} = 1\dfrac{4}{5}$ ◯ _____

㉘ $\dfrac{21}{8} = 3\dfrac{2}{8}$ ◯ _____

㉙ $\dfrac{15}{7} = 1\dfrac{3}{7}$ ◯ _____

Convert the mixed numbers into improper fractions.

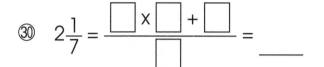

Hints

Follow the steps to convert a mixed number into an improper fraction.

❶ Multiply the whole number by the denominator.

❷ Add the numerator.

❸ Keep the denominator the same.

e.g.

$$5\frac{3}{4} = \frac{\overset{❶}{5 \times 4} \overset{❷}{+ 3}}{4_{❸}} = \frac{23}{4}$$

㉚ $2\frac{1}{7} = \dfrac{\boxed{} \times \boxed{} + \boxed{}}{\boxed{}} = \underline{}$

㉛ $3\frac{5}{8} = \dfrac{\boxed{} \times \boxed{} + \boxed{}}{\boxed{}} = \underline{}$

㉜ $3\frac{1}{3} = \dfrac{\boxed{} \times \boxed{} + \boxed{}}{\boxed{}} = \underline{}$

㉝ $1\frac{5}{6} = \dfrac{\boxed{} \times \boxed{} + \boxed{}}{\boxed{}} = \underline{}$

㉞ $4\frac{1}{4} = \underline{}$ ㉟ $5\frac{1}{2} = \underline{}$ ㊱ $3\frac{2}{5} = \underline{}$ ㊲ $1\frac{3}{7} = \underline{}$

㊳ $3\frac{2}{5} = \underline{}$ ㊴ $2\frac{1}{6} = \underline{}$ ㊵ $3\frac{1}{4} = \underline{}$ ㊶ $2\frac{1}{8} = \underline{}$

Match the equivalent fractions.

㊷

$1\frac{1}{2}$ •   • $\frac{12}{16}$

$4\frac{1}{2}$ •   • $\frac{36}{24}$

$\frac{3}{4}$ •   • $\frac{9}{2}$

$\frac{12}{9}$ •   • $1\frac{1}{3}$

$1\frac{3}{4}$ •   • $\frac{7}{4}$

㊸

$1\frac{3}{8}$ •   • $\frac{11}{8}$

$1\frac{2}{5}$ •   • $1\frac{2}{7}$

$\frac{36}{5}$ •   • $\frac{7}{5}$

$\frac{9}{7}$ •   • $\frac{1}{2}$

$\frac{8}{16}$ •   • $7\frac{1}{5}$

11 Fractions and Decimals

- relating fractions and decimals

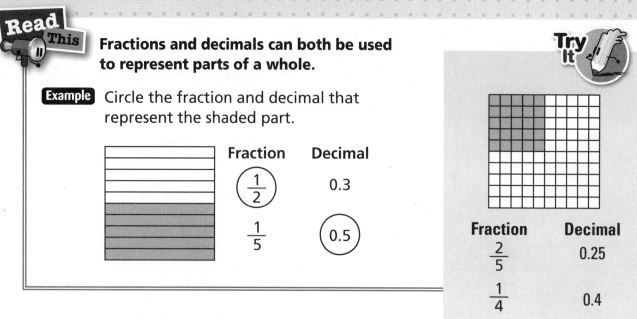

Read This

Fractions and decimals can both be used to represent parts of a whole.

Example Circle the fraction and decimal that represent the shaded part.

Fraction	Decimal
$\frac{1}{2}$ ⟲	0.3
$\frac{1}{5}$	0.5 ⟲

Try It

Fraction	Decimal
$\frac{2}{5}$	0.25
$\frac{1}{4}$	0.4

Write the fraction or decimal for the shaded part of each diagram. Then match the equivalent diagrams.

① **Fraction**   **Decimal**

Colour the diagrams to show the fractions and decimals.

② **0.71**

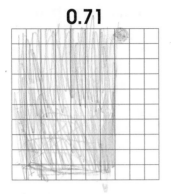

③ **0.48**

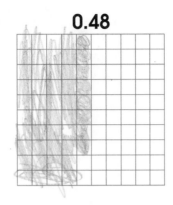

④ **0.2**

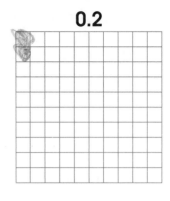

⑤ $\dfrac{7}{10}$

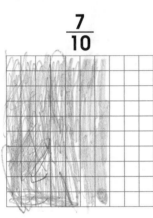

⑥ $\dfrac{85}{100}$

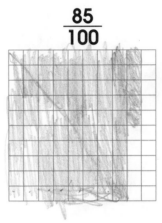

⑦ $\dfrac{13}{100}$

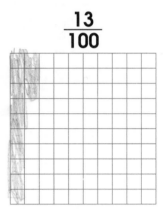

Write a fraction and a decimal to represent the shaded part of each diagram.

⑧

$\dfrac{3}{10}$

⑨

$\dfrac{7}{10}$

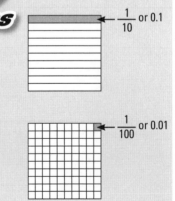

$\dfrac{1}{10}$ or 0.1

$\dfrac{1}{100}$ or 0.01

⑩

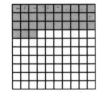

$\dfrac{33}{100}$

⑪

$\dfrac{53}{100}$

⑫

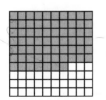

$\dfrac{67}{100}$

⑬

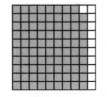

$\dfrac{91}{100}$

⑭

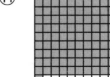

$\dfrac{91}{100}$

Colour the diagrams and do the specified conversions.

⑮ **Fraction ➤ Decimal**

a.

$$\frac{8}{10} = \underline{\hspace{2cm}}$$

b.
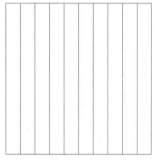
$$\frac{3}{10} = \underline{\hspace{2cm}}$$

c.
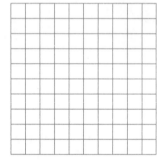
$$\frac{42}{100} = \underline{\hspace{2cm}}$$

d.
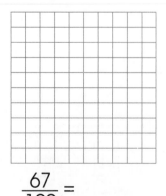
$$\frac{67}{100} = \underline{\hspace{2cm}}$$

⑯ **Decimal ➤ Fraction**

a.
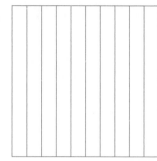
$$0.7 = \underline{\hspace{2cm}}$$

b.

$$0.9 = \underline{\hspace{2cm}}$$

c.
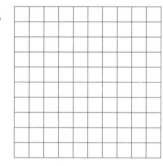
$$0.31 = \underline{\hspace{2cm}}$$

d.
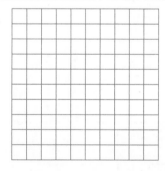
$$0.85 = \underline{\hspace{2cm}}$$

Convert between fractions and decimals. Use the diagrams to help you.

⑰

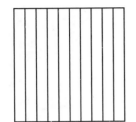

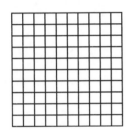

a. $\dfrac{1}{10}$ = _____

b. $\dfrac{6}{10}$ = _____

c. 0.2 = _____

d. 0.5 = _____

e. $\dfrac{43}{100}$ = _____

f. 0.19 = _____

g. 0.77 = _____

h. $\dfrac{87}{100}$ = _____

i. 0.55 = _____

j. $\dfrac{35}{100}$ = _____

k. 0.16 = _____

l. $\dfrac{1}{2}$ = _____

m. $\dfrac{2}{5}$ = _____

n. 0.22 = _____

Compare the fractions and decimals. Write "<", ">", or "=" in the circles.

Use these grids to help compare each pair.

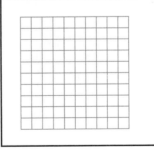
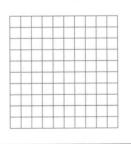

⑱ 0.24 ◯ $\dfrac{42}{100}$

⑲ 0.33 ◯ $\dfrac{3}{10}$

⑳ $\dfrac{3}{4}$ ◯ 0.8

㉑ 0.28 ◯ $\dfrac{1}{5}$

㉒ 0.5 ◯ $\dfrac{1}{2}$

㉓ 0.14 ◯ $\dfrac{14}{100}$

㉔ $\dfrac{35}{100}$ ◯ 0.53

㉕ 0.8 ◯ $\dfrac{4}{5}$

㉖ $\dfrac{6}{10}$ ◯ 0.62

㉗ $\dfrac{1}{1}$ ◯ 1.0

㉘ 0.25 ◯ $\dfrac{1}{4}$

㉙ 0.86 ◯ $\dfrac{21}{25}$

12 Time and Temperature
• reading and writing time and temperature

Time is represented in hours, minutes, and seconds.

Example Write the time.

Time:

$$\underset{\text{hour}}{2} : \underset{\text{minute}}{55} : \underset{\text{second}}{35}$$

Try It

_____ : _____ : _____
hour   minute   second

Write the time shown on each clock.

①

10:40:50

②

4:5:25

③

12:25:

④

2:30:40

⑤

5:50:0

⑥

6:20:30

Draw clock hands to show the given times.

⑦ 9:25:40

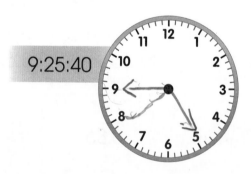

⑧ 11:46:02

SCAN IT!

Convert the times between 12-hour and 24-hour notation.

Hints

⑨ **12-hour notation → 24-hour notation**

a. 7:00 a.m. _____

b. 9:46 a.m. _____

c. 4:00 p.m. _____

d 8:37 p.m. _____

e. 10:08 p.m. _____

f. 11:36 a.m. _____

In 12-hour notation, "a.m." and "p.m." separate time into 12-hour cycles. In 24-hour notation, there are no 12-hour cycles.

To convert time from 12-hour notation into 24-hour notation:

• **between midnight and noon:** remove "a.m."
  e.g. 8:00 a.m. = 8:00

• **between noon and midnight:** add 12 to the hour and remove "p.m."
  e.g. 3:00 p.m. = 15:00

Note: Midnight and noon are special.
• Midnight: 12:00 a.m. = 00:00 or 24:00
• Noon: 12:00 p.m. = 12:00

⑩ **24-hour notation → 12-hour notation**

a. 10:00 _____   b. 02:08 _____

c. 13:21 _____   d. 15:26 _____

e. 21:54 _____   f. 23:39 _____

Write the times using 12-hour notation. Then write the letters to match them with the clocks.

⑪ a. 10:36:20

_____ ◯   b. 20:45:15

_____ ◯

c. 05:21:19

_____ ◯   d. 21:50:03

_____ ◯

Write the temperatures.

⑫

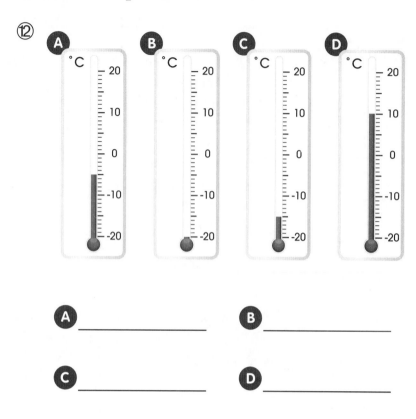

A _____

B _____

C _____

D _____

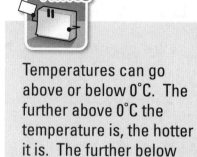

Temperatures can go above or below 0°C. The further above 0°C the temperature is, the hotter it is. The further below 0°C the temperature is, the colder it is.

e.g.

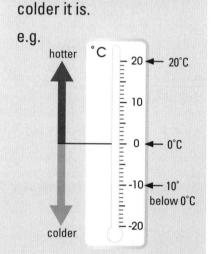

Colour the thermometers to show the temperatures.

⑬

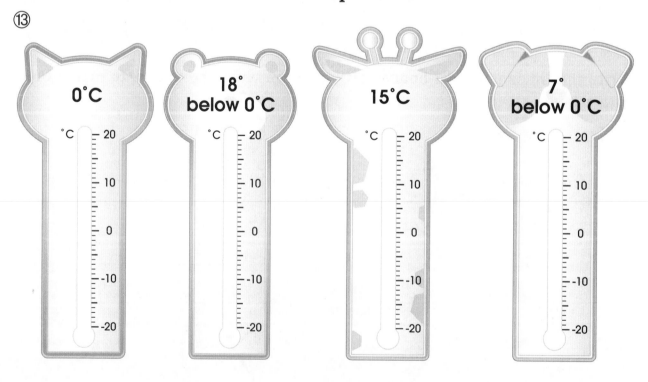

0°C   18° below 0°C   15°C   7° below 0°C

Fill in the blanks and colour the thermometers to show the temperatures.

⑭ The thermometer in the kitchen showed _____°C. After I placed it in the freezer for 2 hours, the temperature _____ by _____°C.
rose/dropped

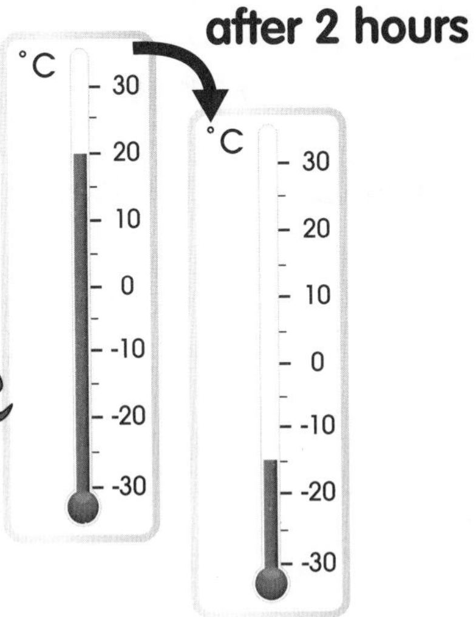

after 2 hours

⑮ **adding hot water**

A can of frozen orange juice had a temperature of _____° _____ 0°C. After adding hot water, the temperature rose by 8°C. The temperature of the juice is now _____°C.
below/above

morning
noon

⑯ The temperature at noon was _____° _____ 0°C. The temperature earlier that morning was 15°C higher. The morning temperature was _____°C.
below/above

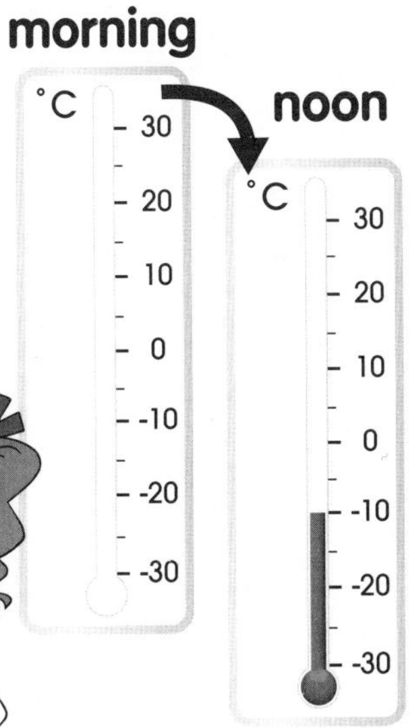

13 Length and Perimeter

• measuring lengths and perimeters

The standard units of measure of length are millimetre (mm), centimetre (cm), metre (m), and kilometre (km).

Example Find the length of the object with a ruler.

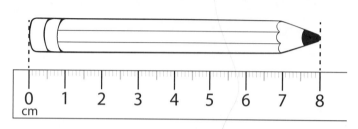

The pencil is 8 cm long.

Try It

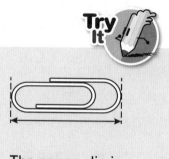

The paper clip is

_____ cm long.

Match the appropriate unit of measure with the thing being measured.

①

 width of a photo •

 length of train tracks •

 height of a house •

 length of an ant •

 distance between two cities •

 length of a belt •

 height of a mountain •

 thickness of a coin •

small unit

↓

• millimetre (mm)

• centimetre (cm)

• metre (m)

• kilometre (km)

large unit

Measure the straws with your ruler.

②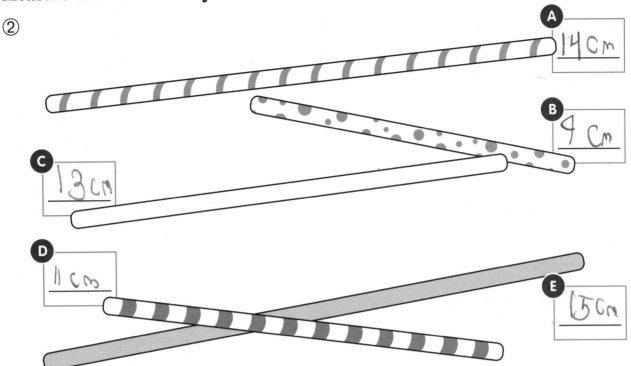

A: 14 cm

B: 9 cm

C: 13 cm

D: 11 cm

E: 15 cm

Draw lines to match the given descriptions.

③ 15 cm long

④ a line 2 cm longer than the given one

⑤ a line 5 cm shorter than the given one

⑥ a line that has the same length as the two lines combined

Do the conversions.

⑦ 2 cm = _____ mm ⑧ 48 cm = _____ mm

⑨ 19 m = _____ cm ⑩ 75 mm = _____ cm

⑪ 7 m = _____ cm ⑫ 5000 m = _____ km

⑬ 60 m = _____ cm ⑭ 300 mm = _____ cm

⑮ 2 mm = _____ cm ⑯ 4200 m = _____ km

⑰ 3 km = _____ m ⑱ 8.2 km = _____ m

Tips

1 cm = 10 mm
1 m = 100 cm
1 km = 1000 m

e.g.
x 1000
5 km = 5000 m

33 cm = 0.33 m
÷ 100

Find the perimeter of each shape.

⑲

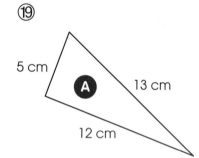

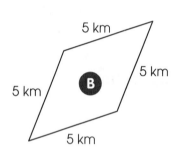

Tips

To find the perimeter of a shape, add up the lengths of all its sides.

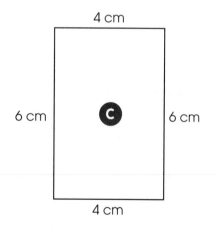

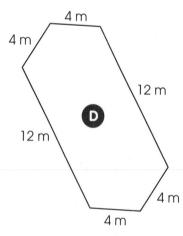

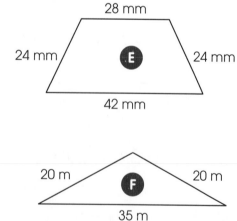

Perimeter

Ⓐ _____ cm   Ⓑ _____   Ⓒ _____

Ⓓ _____   Ⓔ _____   Ⓕ _____

Find the perimeters of the squares and rectangles. Show your work.

Hints

Use these formulas to find the perimeters of squares and rectangles.

Perimeter of a Square:
4 x s

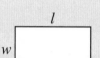

Perimeter of a Rectangle:
2 x l + 2 x w

⑳ **Squares**

a.

3 cm

Perimeter:

4 x _____ = _____ (cm)

b.

5 cm

Perimeter:

_____ = _____

㉑ **Rectangles**

a.

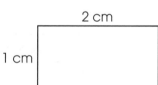

2 cm

1 cm

Perimeter:

2 x _____ + 2 x _____ = _____ (cm)

b.

9 cm

3 cm

Perimeter:

_____ = _____

Find the perimeters of the squares and rectangles using the given measurements.

㉒

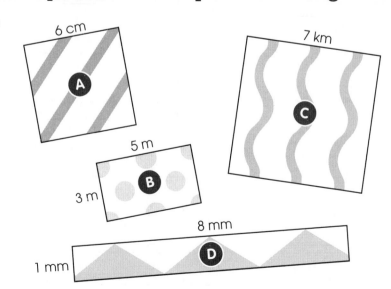

6 cm

A

7 km

C

5 m

B

3 m

8 mm

D

1 mm

Perimeters:

A _____

B _____

C _____

D _____

14 Area

• measuring and calculating areas

Read This

The area is the space occupied by a shape. It is measured in square units such as cm² and m².

Example Find the area.

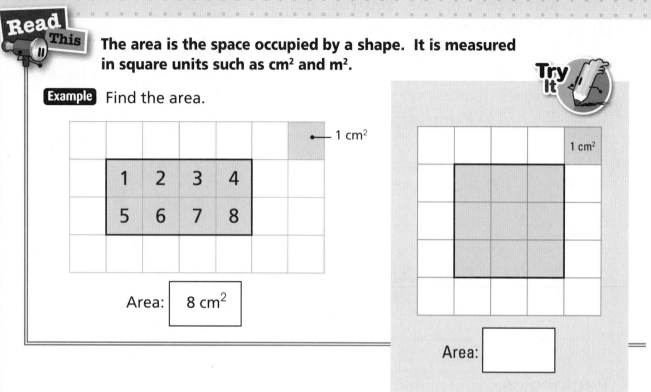

Area: 8 cm²

Try It

Area: _____

Find the areas of the shapes.

①

1 cm²

	Areas
✚	_____ cm²
H	_____
5	_____
⌐	_____
▬	_____

Find the areas of the squares. Show your work.

②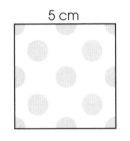

3 cm

Area:

_____ x _____ = _____ (cm²)

Hints

The area of a square is its side length multiplied by itself.

s

Area of a Square:
$s \times s$

③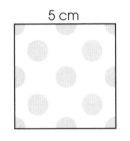

5 cm

Area:

_____

④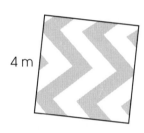

4 m

Area:

_____

⑤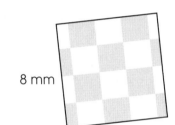

8 mm

Area:

_____

⑥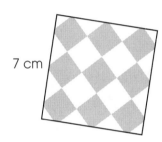

7 cm

Area:

_____

Measure the side lengths of the squares. Then find the areas.

⑦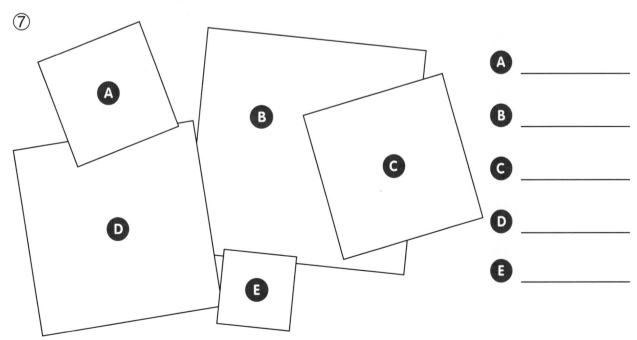

Ⓐ _____

Ⓑ _____

Ⓒ _____

Ⓓ _____

Ⓔ _____

Find the area of each rectangle. Show your work.

⑧

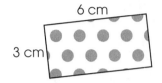

Area:

_____ x _____ = _____ (cm²)

Hints

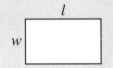

The area of a rectangle is the product of its length and width.

Area of a Rectangle:
l x *w*

⑨

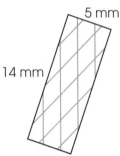

Area:

_____

⑩

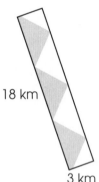

Area:

_____

⑪

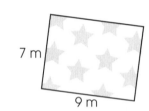

Area:

_____

⑫

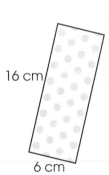

Area:

_____

⑬

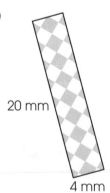

Area:

_____

⑭

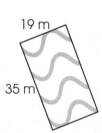

Area:

_____

⑮

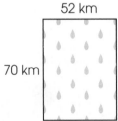

Area:

_____

Measure and find the area of each puzzle piece. Complete the table.

⑯

Puzzle Piece	Dimensions	Area
A	___ cm by ___ cm	___ cm²
B		
C		
D		
E		
F		

15 Volume and Capacity

• finding volumes and capacities

The volume is measured in cubic units such as cm³ and m³. A centimetre cube that measures 1 cm by 1 cm by 1 cm has a volume of 1 cm³.

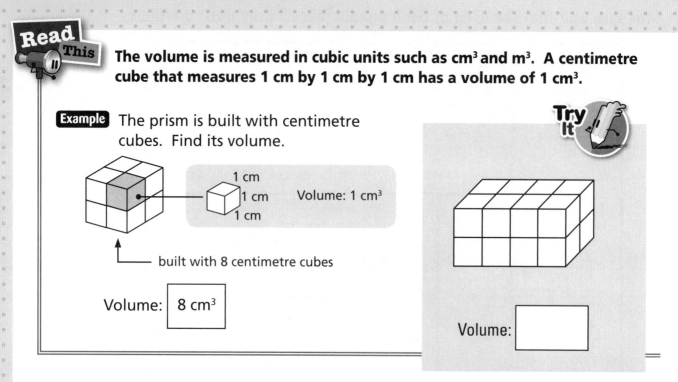

Example The prism is built with centimetre cubes. Find its volume.

1 cm
1 cm
1 cm
Volume: 1 cm³

built with 8 centimetre cubes

Volume: 8 cm³

Try It

Volume: ☐

The rectangular prisms are built with centimetre cubes. Find the volumes.

①

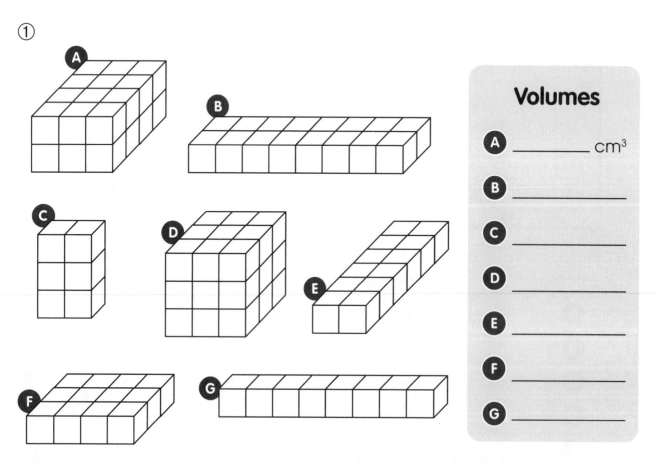

Volumes

A _____ cm³

B _____

C _____

D _____

E _____

F _____

G _____

For each rectangular prism, find the number of centimetre cubes in each layer and count the number of layers in the prism to find the volume. Then circle to complete what the girl says.

②

a layer

Prism	No. of Centimetre Cubes in Each Layer	No. of Layers	Volume (cm³)
A			
B			
C			
D			
E			

The volume of a rectangular prism is equal to the number of centimetre cubes in each layer **multiplied / divided** by the number of layers.

Find the volume of each rectangular prism. Show your work.

Hints

The volume of a rectangular prism is the product of the area of the base multiplied by the height.

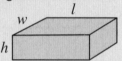

Volume of a Rectangular Prism:

$$l \times w \times h$$

↑
area of the base

③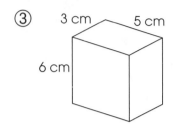

3 cm   5 cm
6 cm

Volume:

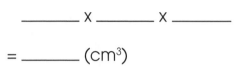

_____ x _____ x _____

= _____ (cm³)

④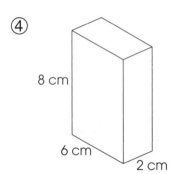

8 cm
6 cm   2 cm

Volume:

_____

= _____

Find the volume of each object.

⑤

20 cm
Cookies
15 cm   5 cm

_____

⑥

Baking Powder
10 cm
2 cm   5 cm

_____

⑦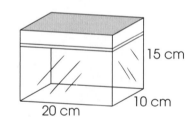

15 cm
20 cm   10 cm

_____

⑧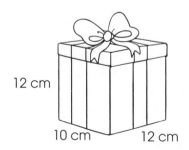

12 cm
10 cm   12 cm

_____

⑨

35 cm
CN TOWER
8 cm   8 cm

_____

⑩

12 cm
10 cm
POPULAR FIGURE!
18 cm
#05 DOG

_____

Find the capacities. Show your work.

⑪

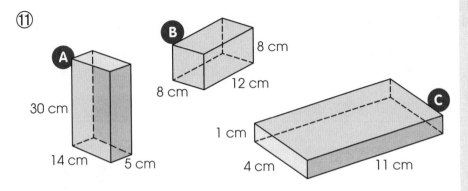

Hints

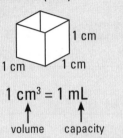

Capacity is the amount of liquid a container can hold. Small capacities are measured in millilitres (mL).

1 cm³ = 1 mL

↑ volume   ↑ capacity

Ⓐ ____ x ____ x ____ = ____ (cm³) = ____ (mL)

Ⓑ _____ = _____ = _____

Ⓒ _____ = _____ = _____

Find the volume of each object by measuring the amount of liquid it displaces.

⑫

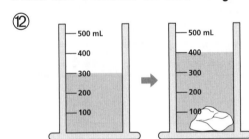

Amount of liquid displaced: ____ mL

Volume of stone: ____ cm³

⑬

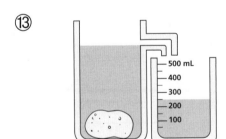

Amount of liquid displaced: ____ mL

Volume of potato: ____ cm³

⑭ A fish tank has a square base measuring 30 cm by 30 cm. When Sam puts a stone into the tank, the water level rises by 5 cm.

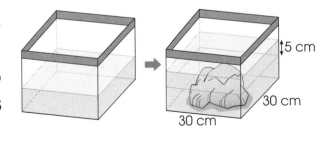

Volume of water displaced: ____ x ____ x ____ = ____ (cm³)

Volume of stone: ____ cm³

16 Angles and Triangles

• measuring and naming angles and triangles

Angles are classified according to their sizes. Here are four types of angles:

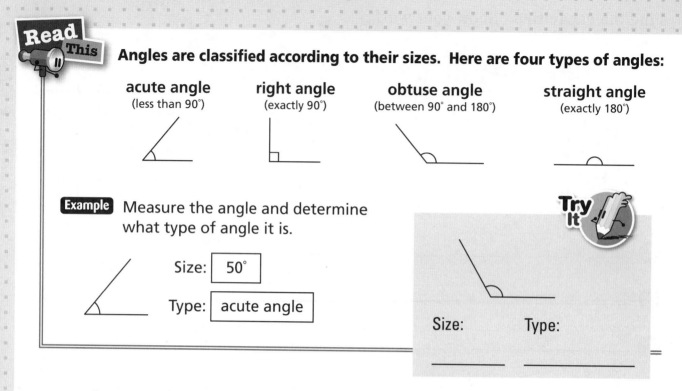

acute angle
(less than 90°)

right angle
(exactly 90°)

obtuse angle
(between 90° and 180°)

straight angle
(exactly 180°)

Example Measure the angle and determine what type of angle it is.

Size: 50°

Type: acute angle

Try It

Size: _____

Type: _____

Measure and record the size of each angle. Then classify it.

①

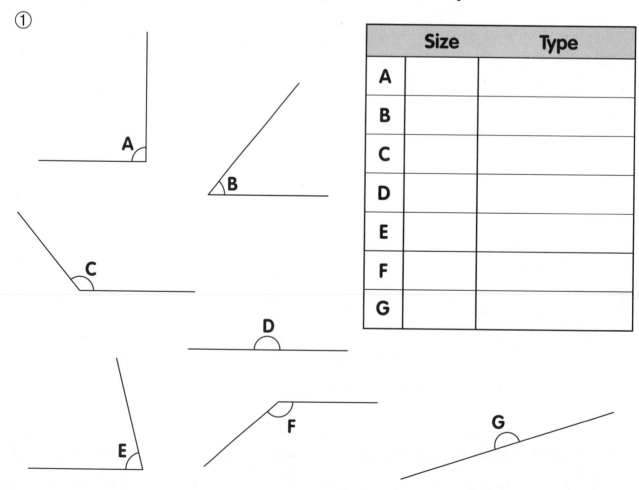

	Size	Type
A		
B		
C		
D		
E		
F		
G		

Draw angles with the given sizes using a protractor. Then classify them.

② 68°

135°

90°

180°

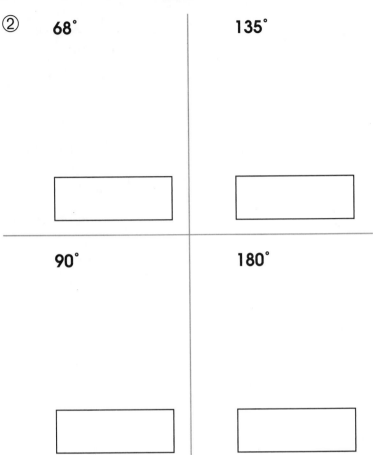

Hints

Follow the steps to draw an angle.

❶ Draw one arm.

＿＿＿＿＿＿

❷ Place the centre of the protractor at one end of the arm and mark the angle.

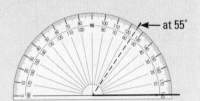

at 55°

❸ Draw the other arm by joining the mark and the end of the first arm.

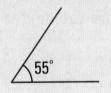

55°

Draw and label the angles with the given descriptions.

③

A an acute angle that is greater than 70°

B an angle that is smaller than a straight angle

C an angle that is greater than an acute angle but smaller than an obtuse angle

Classify the triangles by their angles.

④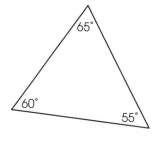

_____

⑤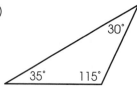

_____

⑥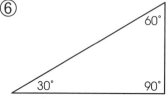

_____

⑦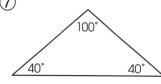

_____

Hints

Classifying Triangles by Angles

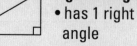 **acute triangle**
• has 3 acute angles

right triangle
• has 1 right angle

obtuse triangle
• has 1 obtuse angle

Measure the angles in each triangle. Then classify the triangle.

⑧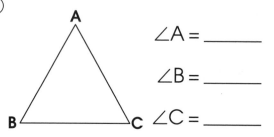

∠A = _____

∠B = _____

∠C = _____

⑨

∠D = _____

∠E = _____

∠F = _____

⑩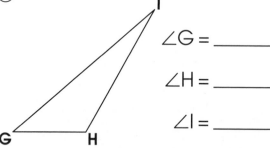

∠G = _____

∠H = _____

∠I = _____

⑪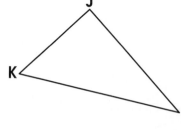

∠J = _____

∠K = _____

∠L = _____

Classify the triangles by their sides.

⑫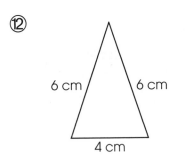

⑬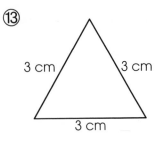

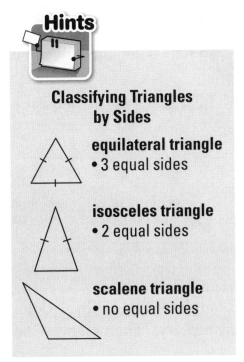

Hints

Classifying Triangles by Sides

equilateral triangle
• 3 equal sides

isosceles triangle
• 2 equal sides

scalene triangle
• no equal sides

_____   _____

⑭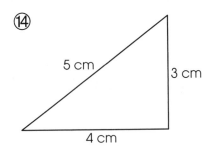

⑮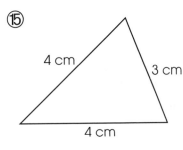

_____   _____

Measure the sides and angles of each triangle. Round your answers to the nearest tenth if needed. Label the triangle. Then classify the triangle by angles and by sides.

⑯

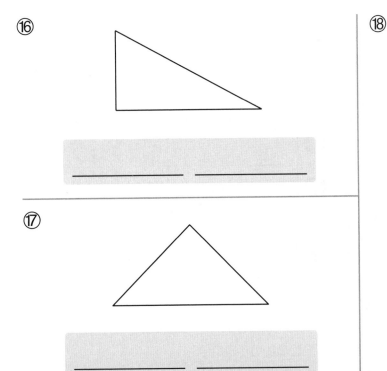

_____   _____

⑰

_____   _____

⑱

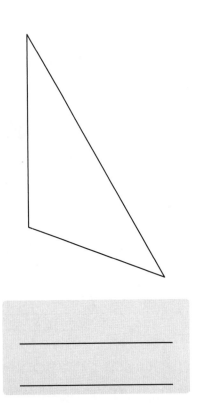

_____

_____

LEVEL 1 – BASIC SKILLS

17 Shapes and Solids

• identifying polygons, prisms, and pyramids

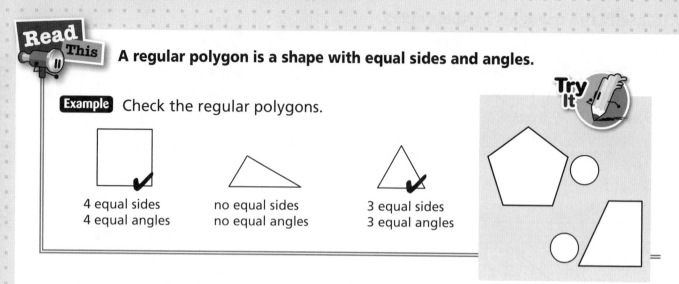

Read This

A regular polygon is a shape with equal sides and angles.

Example Check the regular polygons.

4 equal sides
4 equal angles ✔

no equal sides
no equal angles

3 equal sides
3 equal angles ✔

Try It

Complete the table. Colour the regular polygons and draw their lines of symmetry. Then answer the question.

①

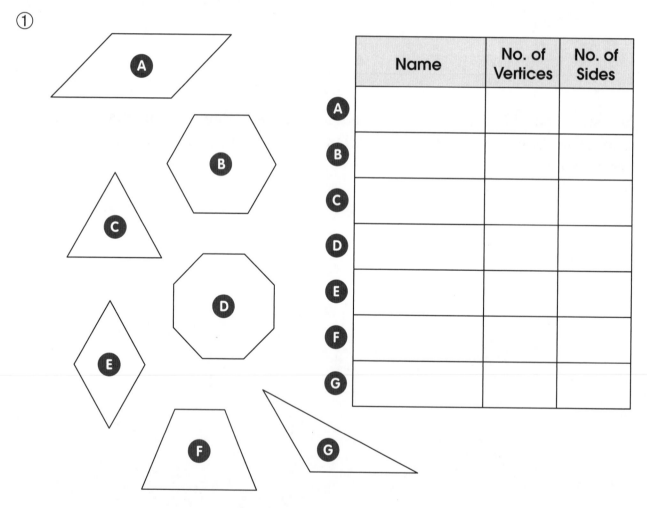

	Name	No. of Vertices	No. of Sides
A			
B			
C			
D			
E			
F			
G			

For a regular polygon, are the number of sides
and the number of lines of symmetry the same? _____

Check the shape that fits each set of descriptions.

②
- all equal sides
- all equal angles
- a quadrilateral

○ square   ○ parallelogram

○ pentagon ○ trapezoid

③
- a quadrilateral
- cannot be a regular polygon

○ triangle   ○ square

○ trapezoid ○ hexagon

Complete the definitions of the terms. Then determine how many vertices, edges, and faces each solid has and name it.

④ 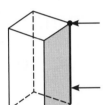 **vertex:** the common end point of ____ or more line segments in a solid
$\frac{2/3}{}$

edge: the line segment where ____ surfaces meet
$\frac{2/3}{}$

face: one of the _____ surfaces of the solid
flat/rough

⑤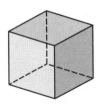

____ vertices

____ edges

____ faces

Name

⑥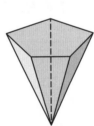

____ vertices

____ edges

____ faces

Name

⑦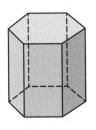

____ vertices

____ edges

____ faces

Name

⑧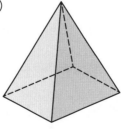

____ vertices

____ edges

____ faces

Name

Look at the pyramids. Complete the table and fill in the blanks.

⑨

No. of Vertices	4	5	6	7
No. of Edges	1	1	1	1
No. of Faces	4	5	6	7
No. of Triangular Faces (excluding the base)	4	4	5	6
Shape of Base	triangle	Square	pentagon	Hexagon

a. The number of _vertices_ and the number of _faces_ are the same.

b. The number of _____ equals the number of sides of the base.

c. The number of _____ is twice the number of sides of the base.

d. The number of vertices is _____ more than the number of sides of the base.

Read the clues and name the solids. Use the given solids to help you.

⑩

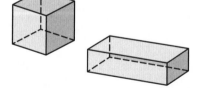   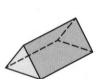

a. 4 faces, 4 vertices, and 6 edges: _____

b. 6 square faces, 8 vertices, and 12 edges: _____

c. 7 faces, 7 vertices, and 12 edges: _____

d. 5 faces, 6 vertices, and 9 edges: _____

e. 6 rectangular faces, 8 vertices, and 12 edges: _____

Match each solid with its net. Write the letters.

⑪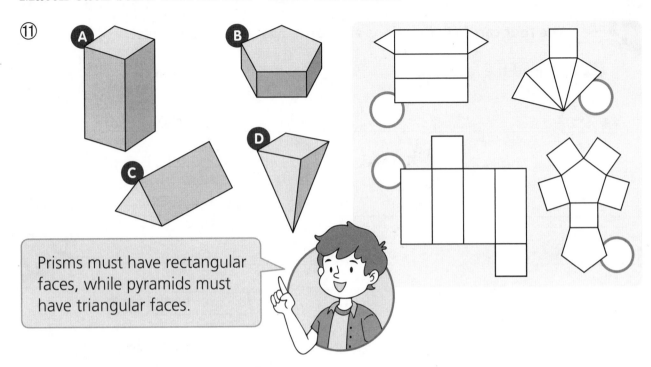

Prisms must have rectangular faces, while pyramids must have triangular faces.

Name the solid that each net forms.

⑫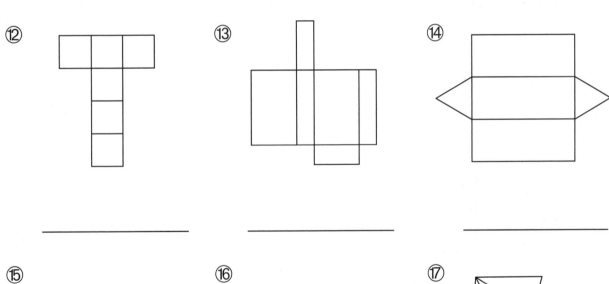

⑬

⑭

⑮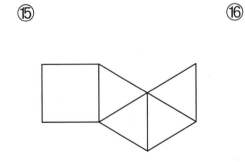

⑯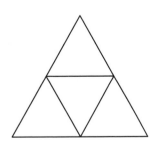

⑰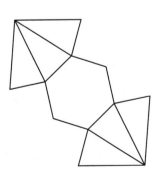

18 Coordinate Systems

• finding locations using cardinal directions and coordinates on a grid

Read This The four cardinal directions are north, east, south, and west.

Example Find the locations.

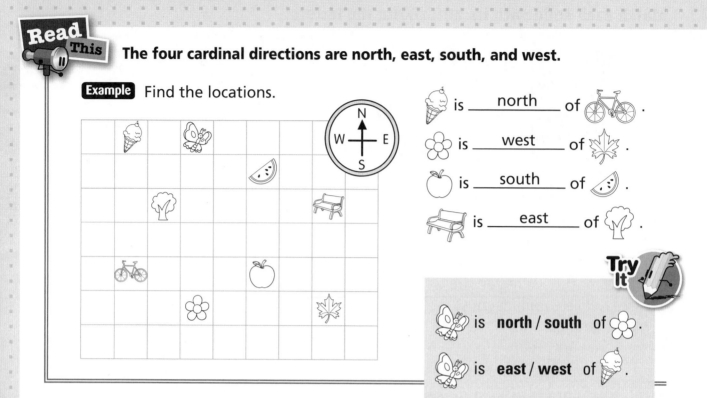

is ____north____ of .

is ____west____ of .

is ____south____ of .

is ____east____ of .

Try It

is **north / south** of .

is **east / west** of .

Read the descriptions. Draw the items on the map.

①

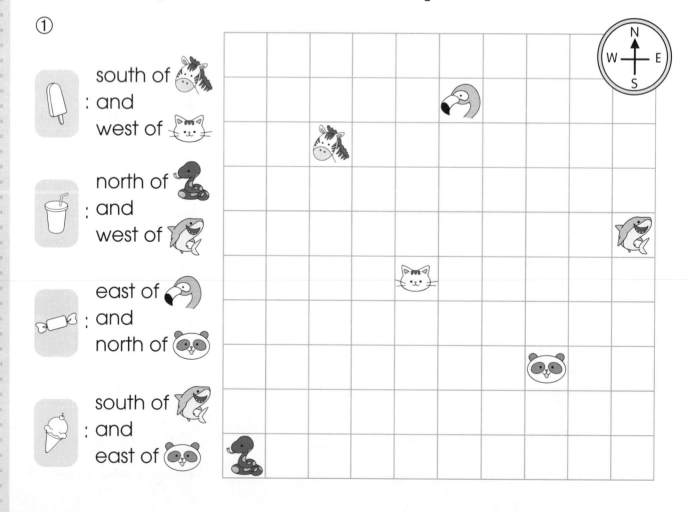

south of : and west of

north of : and west of

east of : and north of

south of : and east of

Use the grid to find the answers.

Hints

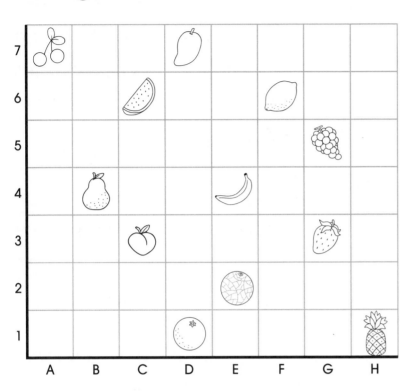

Grid:
a system of squares with letters and numbers that show the exact position of an object or a place

Coordinates:
a letter and number used to locate a place or an object on a specific square on the grid

e.g.

Coordinates of 🍎 : B2

② Write the coordinates of the fruits.

a.

b.

c.

d.

e.

f.

g.

h.

i.

j.

k.

l.

③ Draw the fruits below on the grid.

 F2

 H4

 B6

 D5

④ How many fruits have coordinates with

a. the number 3? _____

b. the letter D? _____

c. the letter E? _____

Use the grid to find the answers.

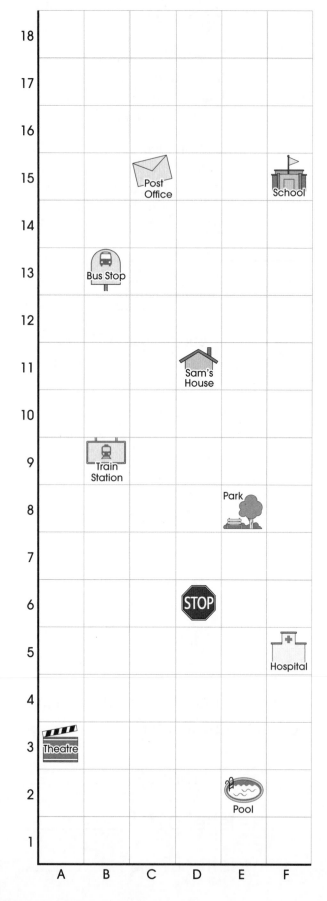

⑤ 👦 is 3 blocks south of the train station. His coordinates are _____ . Draw Sam on the grid.

⑥ 👧 is 4 blocks west of the hospital. Her coordinates are _____ . Draw Lucy on the grid.

⑦ The post office is 3 blocks _____ of the school.
east/west

⑧ The bus stop is 4 blocks _____ of the train station.
north/south

⑨ The theatre is ___ block(s) south and ___ block(s) west of the stop sign.

⑩ The hospital is ___ block(s) north and ___ block(s) east of the pool.

⑪ Sam's house is _____ and _____ of the post office.

⑫ Write the directions for moving between the locations.

a. School to bus stop:

  Move 2 blocks _____
  north/south

  and 4 blocks _____ .
  east/west

b. Park to theatre:

  _____

  _____

c. Pool to stop sign:

  _____

  _____

d. Sam to Sam's house:

  _____

  _____

⑬ **Alex:** I'm at C2. How should I go to get to the park?

_____

⑭ **Jessie:** I'm at F10. How should I go to get to the post office?

_____

⑮ Who is closer to the theatre, Sam or Lucy?   _____

⑯ Who is closer to the train station, Sam or Jessie?   _____

⑰ Who is closer to the hospital, Alex or Jessie?   _____

⑱ Who is closer to the pool, Lucy or Alex?   _____

⑲ Sam visits the park before walking home. Describe Sam's route.

_____

_____

19 Transformations

• describing transformations

Transformations include translations, reflections, and rotations.

Example Trace to show the transformations.

translation

reflection

rotation

Try It

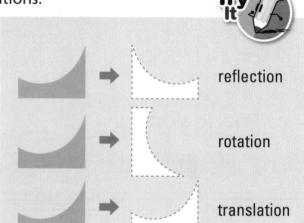

reflection

rotation

translation

Name the transformations.

①

_____

②

_____

③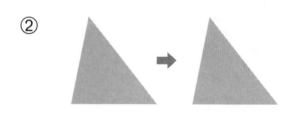

_____

④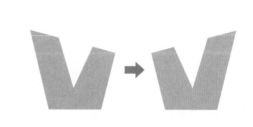

_____

⑤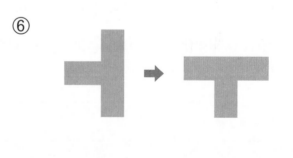

_____

⑥

_____

Describe the translations.

⑦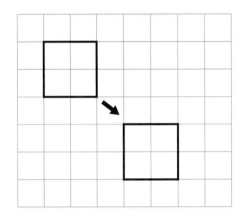

⑧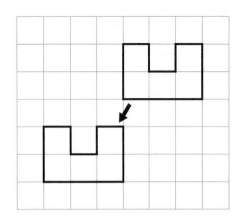

_____ units to the _____
 left/right

and _____ units _____
 up/down

_____

_____

Describe Shape A's translations.

⑨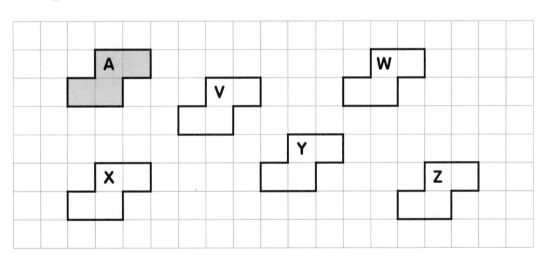

Descriptions

A to V: _____

A to W: _____

A to X: _____

A to Y: _____

A to Z: _____

Draw lines to match the reflections. Then determine whether the reflections are vertical or horizontal.

⑩

   ·

·   _____ reflection

   ·

·   _____ reflection

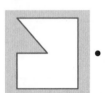   ·

·      _____ reflection

Draw the line of reflection for each pair of figures. Then answer the question.

⑪

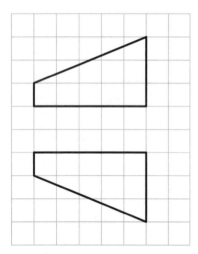

⑫

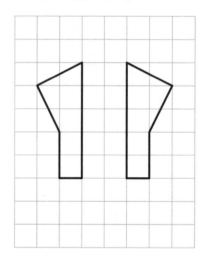

⑬

Count the number of units from the line of reflection to the vertices of each figure. Compare the distances of the corresponding vertices of the figures. What do you notice?

The corresponding vertices in each pair of figures are _____ distance(s) from
_{the same/different}
the line of reflection.

Check the correct descriptions.

⑭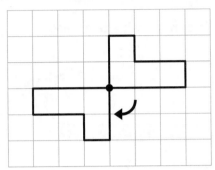

   Ⓐ $\frac{1}{2}$ turn

   Ⓑ $\frac{1}{4}$ turn counterclockwise

⑮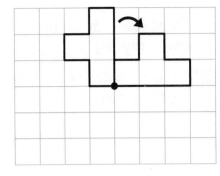

   Ⓐ $\frac{1}{4}$ turn clockwise

   Ⓑ $\frac{1}{4}$ turn counterclockwise

⑯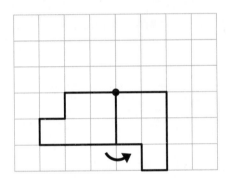

   Ⓐ $\frac{1}{4}$ turn counterclockwise

   Ⓑ $\frac{3}{4}$ turn counterclockwise

⑰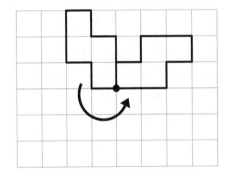

   Ⓐ $\frac{1}{2}$ turn

   Ⓑ $\frac{3}{4}$ turn counterclockwise

Describe the rotation of each shaded shape.

⑱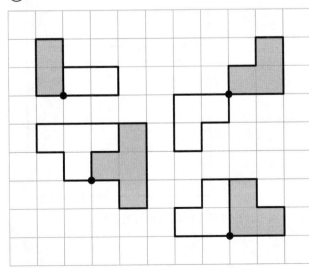

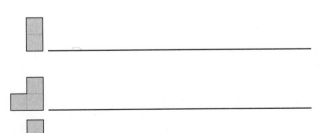

_____

_____

_____

_____

• identifying and extending patterns

Read This

A pattern can be numeric or geometric. It can also be growing or shrinking.

Example Check the correct descriptions of the pattern.

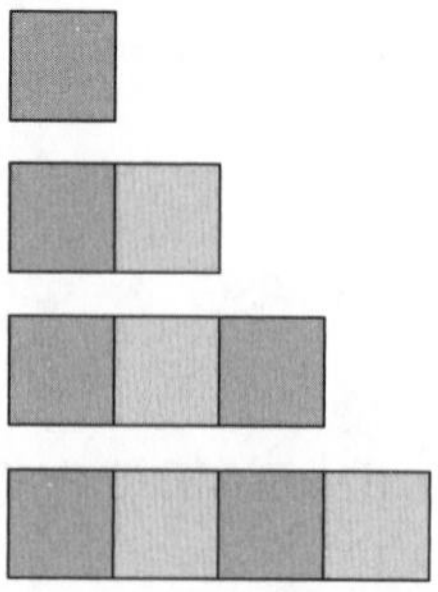

- ◯ numeric pattern
- ✔ geometric pattern
- ✔ growing pattern
- ◯ shrinking pattern

Try It

2, 4, 6, 8, 10

- Ⓐ numeric pattern
- Ⓑ geometric pattern

- Ⓒ growing pattern
- Ⓓ shrinking pattern

Extend the patterns. Then sort the patterns into the correct categories.

① **Pattern A**

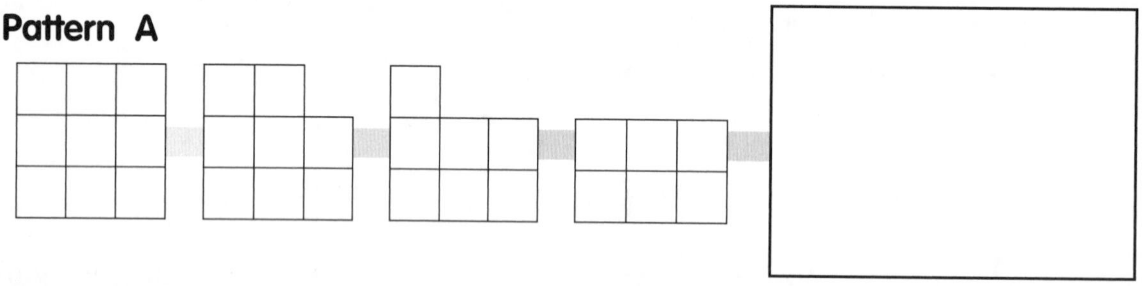

Pattern B

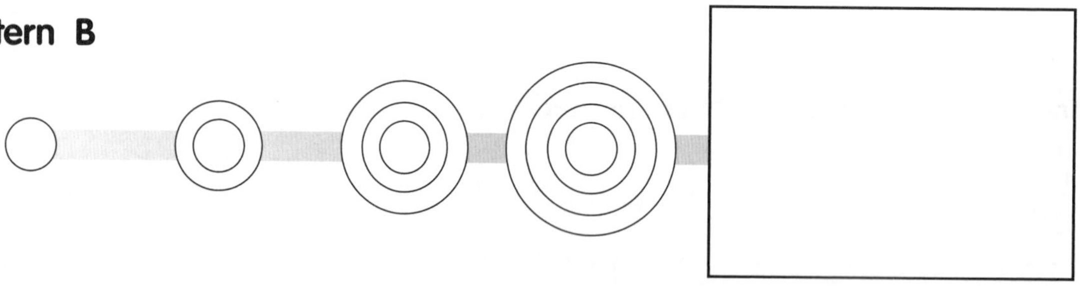

Pattern C

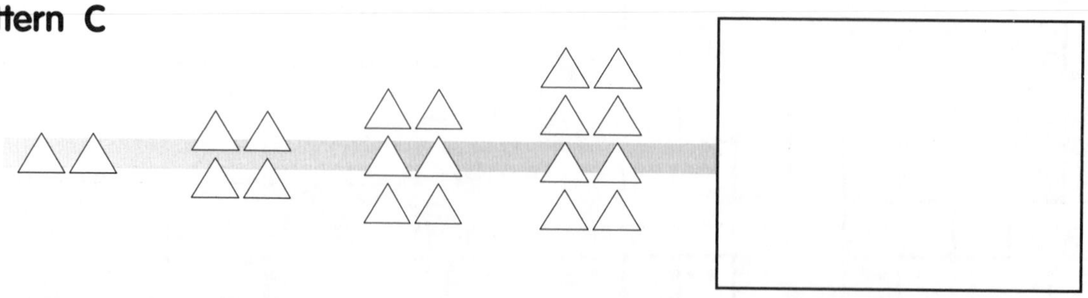

Growing Pattern(s):

_____

Shrinking Pattern(s):

_____

Extend each numeric pattern. Identify whether it is a growing or shrinking pattern.

② 2, 4, 8, 16, 32, _____ , _____   _____ pattern

③ 12, 10, 8, 6, 4, _____ , _____   _____ pattern

④ 2, 4, 12, 14, 42, _____ , _____   _____ pattern

⑤ 729, 243, 81, 27, _____ , _____   _____ pattern

⑥ 5, 10, 11, 22, 23, _____ , _____   _____ pattern

Check the pattern rule that describes each pattern.

⑦ **30, 25, 26, 21, 22**

Pattern Rule:

(A) Start at 30. Subtract 5. Then add 1.

(B) Start at 30. Subtract 5 each time.

A growing pattern involves addition and/or multiplication.

A shrinking pattern involves subtraction and/or division.

⑧ **10, 5, 8, 4, 7**

Pattern Rule:

(A) Start at 10. Subtract 5. Then add 3.

(B) Start at 10. Divide by 2. Then add 3.

⑨ **2, 5, 10, 13, 26**

Pattern Rule:

(A) Start at 2. Add 3. Then multiply by 2.

(B) Start at 2. Add 3. Then add 5.

⑩ **64, 32, 30, 15, 13**

Pattern Rule:

(A) Start at 64. Subtract 32. Then subtract 2.

(B) Start at 64. Divide by 2. Then subtract 2.

Extend each pattern and write its pattern rule.

⑪ 11, 12, 24, 25, 50, 51, _____ , _____

Pattern Rule _____

⑫ 111, 110, 55, 54, 27, 26, _____ , _____

Pattern Rule _____

⑬ 6, 18, 13, 39, 34, 102, _____ , _____

Pattern Rule _____

⑭ 35, 38, 19, 22, 11, 14, _____ , _____

Pattern Rule _____

⑮ 88, 44, 40, 20, 16, 8, _____ , _____

Pattern Rule _____

Draw a line to match each pattern with its pattern rule.

⑯

Pattern	Pattern Rule
16, 11, 22, 17, 34 •	• Start at 16. Multiply by 3. Then divide by 2.
16, 8, 10, 5, 7 •	• Start at 16. Divide by 2. Then add 2.
16, 48, 24, 72, 36 •	• Start at 16. Subtract 5. Then multiply by 2.
16, 17, 51, 52, 156 •	• Start at 16. Add 1. Then multiply by 3.

Farmer Ben has different animals on his farm. Write the number patterns following the given pattern rules. Then use the code to find out what animals are on his farm.

⑰ **Pattern Rule:** Start at 25. Add 1. Then subtract 6.

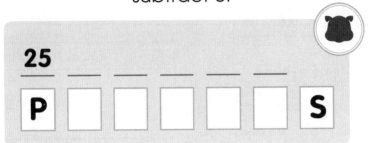

25 __ __ __ __ __ __

| P | | | | | | S |

⑱ **Pattern Rule:** Start at 50. Subtract 5. Then divide by 5.

__ __ __ __

| | | | | S |

⑲ **Pattern Rule:** Start at 9. Subtract 3. Then multiply by 4.

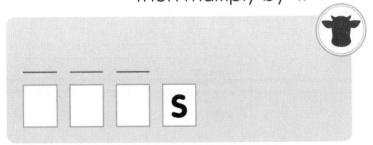

__ __ __

| | | | S |

⑳ **Pattern Rule:** Start at 1. Multiply by 6. Then subtract 3.

__ __ __ __ __

| | | | | | S |

Code

A	31	N	7
B	22	O	6
C	9	P	25
D	50	Q	41
E	15	R	3
F	92	S	18
G	20	T	16
H	1	U	45
I	26	V	10
J	80	W	24
K	4	X	5
L	21	Y	33
M	19	Z	71

21 Simple Equations

• finding missing numbers in equations

A missing number in an equation can be found using the guess-and-check method.

Example Find the missing number.

$1 + \heartsuit = 5$

$\heartsuit = \underline{4}$

Guess	Check (✔ or ✗)	
2	1 + 2 = 3	✗
3	1 + 3 = 4	✗
4	1 + 4 = 5	✔

Try It

$\diamond + 3 = 8$

$\diamond = \underline{\hspace{1cm}}$

Guess	Check (✔ or ✗)

Find the missing numbers using the guess-and-check method.

① $3 + \bigcirc = 10$

$\bigcirc = \underline{\hspace{1cm}}$

Guess	Check (✔ or ✗)

Tips Make reasonable guesses.

e.g. $2 + \triangle = 5$

Reasonable guesses: 2, 3, 4
Unreasonable guesses: 0, 10

② $\square + 2 = 6$

$\square = \underline{\hspace{1cm}}$

Guess	Check (✔ or ✗)

③ $8 - \triangle = 3$

$\triangle = \underline{\hspace{1cm}}$

Guess	Check (✔ or ✗)

④ $\star - 6 = 4$

$\star = \underline{\hspace{1cm}}$

Guess	Check (✔ or ✗)

⑤ $2 + \bigcirc = 10$

$\bigcirc = \underline{\hspace{1cm}}$

Guess	Check (✔ or ✗)

Find the missing numbers. Draw diagrams to help.

⑥ $3 + y = 7$

$y =$ _____

$2 + m = 5$

$m = 3$

⑦ $8 - s = 3$

$s =$ _____

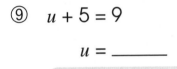

⑧ $k - 3 = 7$

$k =$ _____

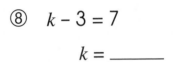

⑨ $u + 5 = 9$

$u =$ _____

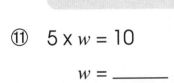

⑩ $12 - m = 5$

$m =$ _____

⑪ $5 \times w = 10$

$w =$ _____

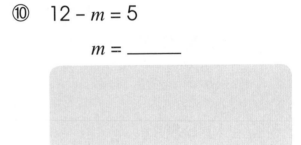

⑫ $9 \div a = 3$

$a =$ _____

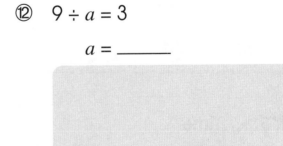

⑬ $p \div 2 = 4$

$p =$ _____

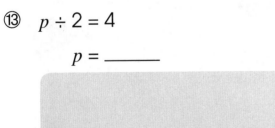

⑭ $f \times 3 = 6$

$f =$ _____

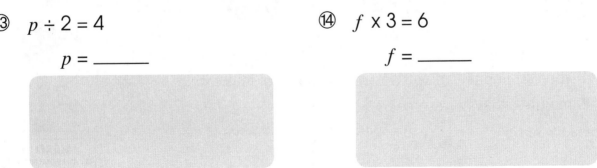

Find the missing numbers using any method. Time yourself.

Addition/Subtraction

⑮ $12 + a = 16$

$a = $ _____

⑯ $20 - k = 7$

$k = $ _____

⑰ $b + 9 = 13$

$b = $ _____

⑱ $m - 6 = 24$

$m = $ _____

⑲ $17 + p = 25$

$p = $ _____

⑳ $q - 11 = 30$

$q = $ _____

㉑ $33 - r = 14$

$r = $ _____

Multiplication/Division

㉒ $5 \times k = 30$

$k = $ _____

㉓ $s \div 9 = 8$

$s = $ _____

㉔ $l \times 3 = 27$

$l = $ _____

㉕ $24 \div n = 3$

$n = $ _____

㉖ $4 \times u = 32$

$u = $ _____

㉗ $27 \div y = 9$

$y = $ _____

㉘ $10 \times d = 40$

$d = $ _____

 Time

_____ minutes

 Time

_____ minutes

If you can find the correct answers in each column within 5 minutes, that's awesome!

AWARD OF AWESOMENESS

Find the missing numbers to solve the riddles.

29. $100 - e = 30$

    $e = \_\_\_\_$

30. $y \times 5 = 40$

    $y = \_\_\_\_$

31. $8 \times w = 96$

    $w = \_\_\_\_$

32. $e \div 9 = 9$

    $e = \_\_\_\_$

33. $49 - d = 13$

    $d = \_\_\_\_$

34. $18 - n = 5$

    $n = \_\_\_\_$

35. $62 + o = 88$

    $o = \_\_\_\_$

36. $h + 41 = 69$

    $h = \_\_\_\_$

Do your work here.

I'm the sweetest and most romantic fruit. What am I?

$\overline{\quad}$ $\overline{\quad}$ $\overline{\quad}$ $\overline{\quad}$ $\overline{\quad}$ $\overline{\quad}$ $\overline{\quad}$ $\overline{\quad}$
 28   26   13   70   8   36   81   12

37. $18 \times g = 54$

    $g = \_\_\_\_$

38. $100 \div p = 5$

    $p = \_\_\_\_$

39. $l - 16 = 33$

    $l = \_\_\_\_$

40. $e + 18 = 40$

    $e = \_\_\_\_$

41. $t \div 8 = 3$

    $t = \_\_\_\_$

42. $g \times 4 = 100$

    $g = \_\_\_\_$

43. $64 - n = 32$

    $n = \_\_\_\_$

44. $49 \div a = 7$

    $a = \_\_\_\_$

Do your work here.

They say that I'm a vegetable that grows eggs. What am I?

$\overline{\quad}$ $\overline{\quad}$ $\overline{\quad}$ $\overline{\quad}$ $\overline{\quad}$ $\overline{\quad}$ $\overline{\quad}$ $\overline{\quad}$
 22   3   25   20   49   7   32   24

22 Mean, Median, and Mode

- finding the mean, median, and mode

Read This

The mean is the sum of a set of data values divided by the number of data values in the set. The mean is commonly referred to as the "average".

Example Find the mean.

| 4 | 8 | 6 | 10 | 7 |

sum of data values   no. of data values

Mean: $(4 + 8 + 6 + 10 + 7) \div 5$

= 7

Try It

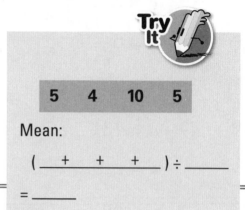

| 5 | 4 | 10 | 5 |

Mean:

(___ + ___ + ___) ÷ _____

= _____

Find the mean of each set of data. Then answer the questions.

①

A

| 11 | 5 | 6 | 10 |

Mean:

(_____) ÷ _____

= _____

B

| 5 | 9 | 4 | 7 | 8 | 3 |

Mean:

_____

= _____

C

| 4 | 6 | 10 | 7 | 8 |

Mean:

_____

= _____

D

| 9 | 8 | 4 | 6 | 3 | 7 | 12 |

Mean:

_____

= _____

② a. Which set of data has the greatest mean? _____

b. Which set of data has the smallest mean? _____

c. Is it true that a data set with more data values must also have a greater mean? _____

d. Is it true that two data sets with the same mean must also have the same number of data values? _____

The data sets are arranged in order. Find the mean, median, and mode of each.

③
$$8 \quad 11 \quad 12 \quad 12 \quad 16 \quad 19$$

Mean: _____

Median: _____   Mode: _____

④
$$11 \quad 15 \quad 28 \quad 32 \quad 32 \quad 32$$

Mean: _____

Median: _____   Mode: _____

Find the mean, median, and mode of each set of data.

⑤ 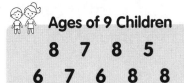 **Ages of 9 Children**
$$8 \quad 7 \quad 8 \quad 5$$
$$6 \quad 7 \quad 6 \quad 8 \quad 8$$

Mean: _____ years old

Median: _____

Mode: _____

⑥ 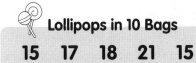 **Lollipops in 10 Bags**
$$15 \quad 17 \quad 18 \quad 21 \quad 15$$
$$18 \quad 19 \quad 20 \quad 18 \quad 19$$

Mean: _____ lollipops

Median: _____

Mode: _____

⑦ 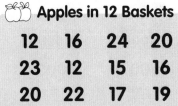 **Apples in 12 Baskets**
$$12 \quad 16 \quad 24 \quad 20$$
$$23 \quad 12 \quad 15 \quad 16$$
$$20 \quad 22 \quad 17 \quad 19$$

Mean: _____ apples

Median: _____

Mode: _____

⑧ 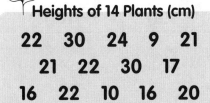 **Heights of 14 Plants (cm)**
$$22 \quad 30 \quad 24 \quad 9 \quad 21$$
$$21 \quad 22 \quad 30 \quad 17$$
$$16 \quad 22 \quad 10 \quad 16 \quad 20$$

Mean: _____ cm

Median: _____

Mode: _____

Answer the questions.

⑨ The children recorded their cousins' allowances. Find the mean, median, and mode allowances of

a. Jane's cousins.

_____ _____ _____
   mean   median   mode

b. Leo's cousins.

_____ _____ _____
   mean   median   mode

Jane's Cousins		Leo's Cousins	
$7	$9	$4	$8
	$4	$5	$5
$4	$6	$7	$1

⑩ Don spilled some paint on his report card, covering his mark in Math. He got 78 in English, 86 in Social Studies, 92 in Science, and 68 in French. His average mark was 76.

a. What was his mark in Math?

b. If he wanted an average mark of 77, what mark would he need to get in Math?

His mark was _____ .

He would need to get _____ .

⑪ Tim has a mean of 135 cards in 4 boxes. Which 4 of these boxes are his?

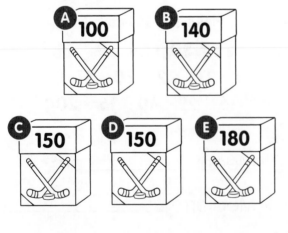

Boxes _____ are his.

⑫ Elaine has a mean of 1235 g of flour in 4 bags. Which 4 of these bags are hers?

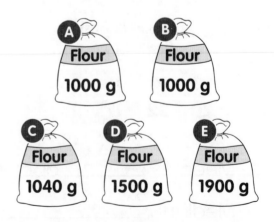

Bags _____ are hers.

92   Complete MathSmart (**Grade 5**)

Answer the questions. Then check the correct answers.

⑬ Lori was trying to improve her running speed. She practised every day for 4 weeks. Her times were recorded in the table.

Lori's Running Times

Week / Day	1	2	3	4
Sun	127 s	110 s	124 s	100 s
Mon	117 s	126 s	106 s	125 s
Tue	120 s	112 s	98 s	105 s
Wed	105 s	104 s	110 s	104 s
Thu	110 s	108 s	106 s	100 s
Fri	105 s	110 s	106 s	104 s
Sat	100 s	121 s	106 s	104 s

Find the mean, median, and mode running times of each week.

	Week 1	Week 2	Week 3	Week 4
Mean				
Median				
Mode				

⑭ Her mean running time for Week 5 was 115 s. What was her total running time that week?

   Ⓐ 575 s   Ⓑ 1150 s   Ⓒ 805 s

⑮ In Week 6, her times for the first 6 days were 105 s, 166 s, 132 s, 128 s, 113 s, and 120 s. How long should Lori run on the 7th day if she wants the mean running time of the week to be 124 s?

   Ⓐ 104 s   Ⓑ 124 s   Ⓒ 109 s

⑯ The median and mode running times were both 112 s for Week 7. Which data set shows Lori's running times for Week 7?

   Ⓐ 125 s 103 s 112 s 125 s 112 s 125 s 103 s

   Ⓑ 106 s 112 s 110 s 112 s 123 s 114 s 128 s

23 Probability

- determining probability

A possible outcome is an outcome that is a possible result of an experiment.

Example List the possible outcomes.

The coin is tossed.

Possible outcomes: | heads, tails |

A card is picked.

Possible outcomes:

_____

List the possible outcomes of each experiment.

① A ball is drawn.

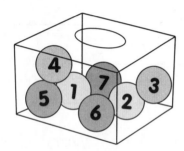

Possible outcomes:

_____

② The spinner is spun.

Possible outcomes:

_____

③ The dice is rolled.

Possible outcomes:

_____

④ A card is picked.

Possible outcomes:

_____

Help each child pick the set with outcomes that are equally likely. Check the circle. Then list all the possible outcomes in that set.

⑤

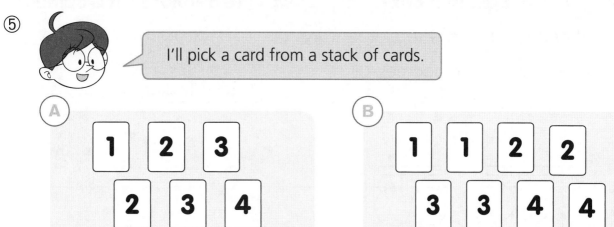

Possible outcomes: _____

⑥

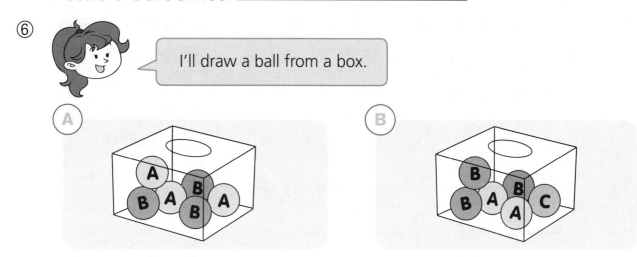

Possible outcomes: _____

⑦

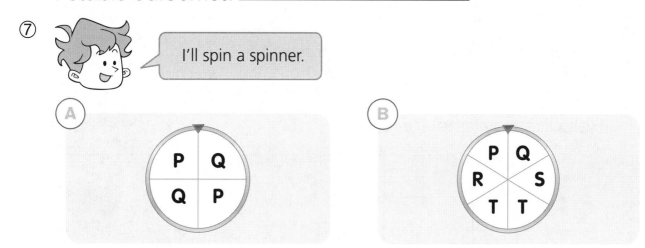

Possible outcomes: _____

Draw or colour to make the diagrams match the descriptions.

⑧
8 Balls in a Box

Possible outcomes: red, green

Equally likely outcomes: all

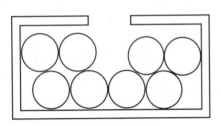

⑨
10 Sections on a Spinner

Possible outcomes:
A, B, C, D, E

Equally likely outcomes: all

⑩
4 Cards in a Pile

Possible outcomes: J, Q, K

Equally likely outcomes: J, Q

⑪
7 Marbles in a Bag

Possible outcomes:
red, blue, green

Equally likely outcomes:
blue, green

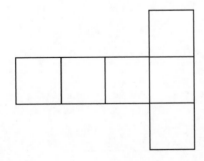

⑫
I made this net to form a dice. The possible outcomes of this dice when rolled are 1, 2, 3, and 4. The outcomes of 1 and 4 are equally likely.

Help the boy label the dice.

Read what the girl says and try the experiment. Draw a tree diagram, list the possible outcomes, and check the correct answers.

⑬

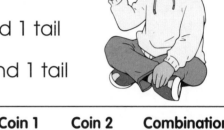

> Ask an adult for 2 coins. Toss them both at the same time until you find the 3 possible outcomes.

Check the possible outcomes.

(A) 2 heads   (B) 1 head and 1 tail

(C) 2 tails   (D) 2 heads and 1 tail

⑭ Draw a tree diagram to show all the possible outcomes of the experiment.

Possible outcomes:

_____

Coin 1	Coin 2	Combination

⑮ What is the probability of getting

a. 2 heads?

(A) $\frac{1}{2}$ (B) $\frac{1}{3}$ (C) $\frac{1}{4}$ (D) $\frac{4}{1}$

b. 2 tails?

(A) $\frac{1}{2}$ (B) $\frac{1}{3}$ (C) $\frac{1}{4}$ (D) $\frac{4}{1}$

c. no heads?

(A) $\frac{1}{2}$ (B) $\frac{1}{3}$ (C) $\frac{1}{4}$ (D) $\frac{4}{1}$

d. 1 head and 1 tail?

(A) $\frac{1}{2}$ (B) $\frac{1}{3}$ (C) $\frac{1}{4}$ (D) $\frac{4}{1}$

e. no tails?

(A) $\frac{1}{2}$ (B) $\frac{1}{3}$ (C) $\frac{1}{4}$ (D) $\frac{4}{1}$

LEVEL 2
FURTHER YOUR UNDERSTANDING

1 Operations with Whole Numbers

- solving operations with whole numbers

When an expression involves both addition and subtraction, remember to solve it from left to right.

e.g. ——————→ Solve from left to right.

$5 - 1 + 7$

$= 4 + 7$

$= 11$

Example Find the answer.

$2419 + 1627 - 3049$

$= \boxed{4046} - 3049$

$= \boxed{997}$

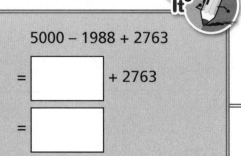

Try It

$5000 - 1988 + 2763$

$= \boxed{} + 2763$

$= \boxed{}$

Find the answers.

① $79 + 65 - 92 + 117 = $ _____

② $250 - 49 - 27 + 88 = $ _____

③ $3625 + 1037 - 1148 = $ _____

④ $7219 - 2813 - 1124 = $ _____

⑤ $8000 - 1709 + 268 = $ _____

⑥ $3627 + 2373 - 419 = $ _____

⑦ $983 + 782 - 1454 = $ _____

⑧ $1628 + 193 + 2411 = $ _____

⑨ $3726 - 1235 + 1642 = $ _____

⑩ $4090 - 2887 + 3146 = $ _____

Find the missing numbers.

⑪ _____ $+ 1182 = 4907$

⑫ $3048 + $ _____ $= 5000$

⑬ $4100 - $ _____ $= 1369$

⑭ _____ $- 2191 = 3209$

⑮ _____ $+ 2683 = 3144$

⑯ $1489 + $ _____ $= 5218$

⑰ $2946 - $ _____ $= 1445$

⑱ _____ $- 1687 = 4253$

Tips Addition and subtraction are closely related.

eg. $\underline{3} + 2 = 5$

$5 - 2 = 3$

$\underline{9} - 1 = 8$

$1 + 8 = 9$

Multiply or divide.

⑲ $595 \div 7 =$ _85_

⑳ $34 \times 18 =$ _612_

㉑ $438 \div 6 =$ _73_

㉒ $325 \div 5 =$ _65_

㉓ $26 \times 26 =$ _676_

㉔ $873 \div 3 =$ _291_

㉕ $43 \times 17 =$ _731_

㉖ $36 \times 19 =$ _684_

㉗ $736 \div 8 =$ _92_

㉘ $365 \div 5 =$ _73_

㉙ $17 \times 65 =$ _1.05_

㉚ $38 \times 49 =$ _____

㉛ $54 \times 27 =$ _____

㉜ $297 \div 9 =$ _____

Do your work here.

㉝ $280 \div 5 \times 17 =$ _____

㉞ $22 \times 20 \div 8 =$ _____

㉟ $15 \times 33 \div 5 =$ _____

㊱ $846 \div 6 \div 3 =$ _____

㊲ $639 \div 9 \times 12 =$ _____

㊳ $45 \times 21 \div 7 =$ _____

㊴ $32 \times 19 \div 8 =$ _____

㊵ $504 \div 9 \times 22 =$ _____

Do the division with remainders. Then check your answers using multiplication and addition.

41. 894 ÷ 5 = ________ R ____

Check ______ x ______ + ______ = ______
quotient divisor remainder

42. 120 ÷ 7 = __________

Check ____________________

43. 737 ÷ 2 = __________

Check ____________________

44. 372 ÷ 9 = __________

Check ____________________

45. 149 ÷ 6 = __________

Check ____________________

Tips To find out whether an answer to a division question is correct, multiply the quotient by the divisor and add the remainder. If you get the original dividend, the answer is correct.

e.g. 415 ÷ 3 = 138 R 1
dividend divisor quotient remainder

Is the answer above correct?

Check

138 x 3 + 1 = 415

same as dividend

So, it is correct.

Do the calculations mentally. Put a check mark in the box if the answer is correct; otherwise, write the correct answer in the box.

46. 2 x 10 x 7 = 140 ☐

47. 200 ÷ 10 ÷ 5 = 4 ☐

48. 35 – 8 + 7 = 20 ☐

49. 78 + 12 – 20 = 70 ☐

(50) 300 ÷ 30 x 2 = 5 ☐

(51) 99 ÷ 9 x 2 = 22 ☐

(52) 100 x 2 ÷ 200 = 1 ☐

(53) 124 ÷ 2 x 6 = 372 ☐

(54) 5000 ÷ 50 ÷ 100 = 10 ☐

(55) 5 x 29 x 2 = 290 ☐

(56) 400 ÷ 100 x 5 = 200 ☐

(57) 27 000 ÷ 300 = 900 ☐

(58) 540 – 240 – 100 – 150 = 150 ☐

(59) 2000 x 35 = 7000 ☐

(60) 324 – 24 + 224 = 524 ☐

(61) 501 + 398 – 199 = 650 ☐

Do the division. Match the letters with the remainders to decode what the boy is saying.

62) $235 \div 2 =$ _____ [w]

63) $482 \div 5 =$ _____ [l]

64) $975 \div 8 =$ _____ [e]

65) $926 \div 9 =$ _____ [o]

66) $435 \div 6 =$ _____ [d]

67) $599 \div 7 =$ _____ [n]

If you can decode my message, ___ ___ ___ ___
               1   7   2   2
___ ___ ___ ___ !
 3   8   4   7

Calculate and colour the answers in the number puzzle horizontally or vertically. Then answer the question.

68) $1539 - 1158 =$ _____

69) $1234 - 999 =$ _____

70) $58 \times 21 =$ _____

71) $2345 + 999 =$ _____

72) $720 \div 6 =$ _____

73) $15 \times 14 =$ _____

74) $3456 + 1398 =$ _____

75) $1981 - 1975 =$ _____

76) $17 \times 11 =$ _____

77) $203 \div 7 =$ _____

78) $576 \div 8 =$ _____

2	3	5	1	8	7
5	1	2	1	8	4
7	2	3	1	1	8
2	9	8	2	2	5
0	7	1	0	1	4
3	3	4	4	0	6

Add the uncoloured numbers to find how many stickers I have.

_____ stickers

LEVEL 2 – FURTHER YOUR UNDERSTANDING

2 Adding and Subtracting Decimals

- adding and subtracting decimals

Read This

Order of Operations

Remember to add and subtract in order from left to right.

e.g. $2.5 - 0.4 + 1.3$

$= 2.1 + 1.3$

$= 3.4$

Example Find the answer.

$2.5 + 1.82 - 0.95$ ⟵ Solve from left to right.

$= 4.32 - 0.95$

$= 3.37$

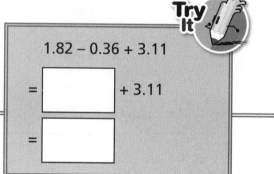

Try It

$1.82 - 0.36 + 3.11$

$=$ ⬚ $+ 3.11$

$=$ ⬚

Find the answers. Show your steps.

① $5.2 - 3.8 + 17.5$

$=$ _____ $+ 17.5$

$=$ _____

② $3.75 - 1.25 - 0.5$

③ $5.99 - 3.99 + 4.99$

④ $12 - 0.5 + 2.52$

⑤ $7.55 + 3.45 - 0.56$

⑥ $3 - 0.75 - 0.75$

Do your work here.

Jane and Dan are playing a game. Find the answers and colour them on the cards to find out who wins the game.

⑦ The player with a row, column, or diagonal coloured wins the game.

a. **Jane's Card**

$1.9 - 0.5 - 1.4$ = _____

$9.92 + 4.01 - 6$ = _____

$13.25 - 2.5 + 5.2$ = _____

$20.72 - 4 + 7.81$ = _____

$45.85 + 7.05 + 5.15$ = _____

$70.4 - 28.92 + 4$ = _____

$12.3 + 14.07 - 1.92$ = _____

10.14	15.95	4.99	16.73
7.93	58.05	45.48	24.53
0.86	20.11	1.07	24.45
9.7	4.99	0	30.51

b. **Dan's Card**

$1 - 0.09 + 3.78$ = _____

$1.2 + 5.6 - 4$ = _____

$7.1 + 3 - 5.09$ = _____

$2.09 + 0.92 - 0.08$ = _____

$7.3 + 2.9 - 5.4$ = _____

$22 - 3.5 - 9.7$ = _____

$6.73 + 18.45 - 23.38$ = _____

9.8	1.8	15.19	8.8
15.6	4.69	48.56	2.8
3.09	2.93	5.01	9.19
4.8	10.8	35.2	3.8

_____ wins!

Do the addition. Then estimate to check your answers. Show your work.

⑧ 7.1 + 3.62 = ☐

Sum: | Estimate:

When estimating, round the numbers in the question to the nearest one.

e.g.   8.53 $\xrightarrow[\text{round to}]{}$ 9

⑨ 0.09 + 5.78 = ☐

Sum: | Estimate:

⑩ 7.3 + 2.95 = ☐

Sum: | Estimate:

⑪ 17.55 + 3.08 = ☐

Sum: | Estimate:

⑫ 28.07 + 26.9 = ☐

Sum: | Estimate:

Find the difference of each pair of numbers. Then estimate to check your answer.

⑬
8.02
13

Difference:

⑭
15.25
6.75

Difference:

⑮
29.63
24.96

Difference:

⑯
45.92
26.31

Difference:

Estimate: Estimate: Estimate: Estimate:

Change the order of operations to make friendly numbers. Then find the answers.

⑰ 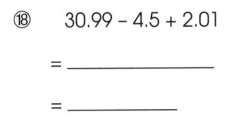 18.25 + 6.99 – 8.25

= _____

= _____

= _____

⑱ 30.99 – 4.5 + 2.01

= _____

= _____

= _____

Tips

To help solve a problem, try changing the order of operations. Move the number together with the sign before it to make a friendly number that is easy to work with.

e.g.　2.5 – 1.96 + 1.5

= 2.5 + 1.5 – 1.96 ← order of operations changed

= 4 – 1.96

= 2.04

⑲ 9.45 – 2.33 + 3.55

⑳ 16.12 + 6.8 – 8.12

㉑ 17.46 – 8.99 – 5.46

㉒ 2.05 + 9.46 + 7.95

㉓ 10.99 – 2.35 + 3.01

㉔ 28.31 – 1.49 – 5.31

㉕ 8.95 – 2.34 + 11.05 + 4.5

㉖ 39.65 – 19.38 + 21.35 + 4.8

LEVEL 2 – FURTHER YOUR UNDERSTANDING

3 Multiplying and Dividing Decimals

- multiplying and dividing decimals by 10, 100, and 1000

Read This

a decimal × 10/100/1000
- move the decimal point 1/2/3 places to the right respectively

a decimal ÷ 10/100/1000
- move the decimal point 1/2/3 places to the left respectively

Example Solve.

$2.5 \times 10 = \underline{25}$
1 zero

Move the decimal point 1 place to the right.

$2.5 \div 100 = \underline{0.025}$
2 zeros

Move the decimal point 2 places to the left.

Try It

0.49 × 100 = ☐

36 ÷ 100 = ☐

Multiply or divide.

① 7.34 × 10 = _____

② 9.23 ÷ 10 = _____

③ 123.4 ÷ 1000 = _____

④ 2.42 × 10 = _____

⑤ 36.9 ÷ 100 = _____

⑥ 1.2 × 100 = _____

⑦ 0.15 × 100 = _____

⑧ 80.8 ÷ 10 = _____

⑨ 342 ÷ 100 = _____

⑩ 34.29 × 1000 = _____

⑪ 1.25 × 100 = _____

⑫ 0.02 × 100 = _____

⑬ 0.4 × 1000 = _____

⑭ 1.18 × 1000 = _____

⑮ 0.06 × 100 = _____

⑯ 12.5 ÷ 10 = _____

⑰ 0.22 × 10 = _____

⑱ 63.5 × 10 = _____

⑲ 500 ÷ 1000 = _____

⑳ 390 ÷ 100 = _____

Write "×" or "÷" to complete the operation.

㉑ $3.95 \bigcirc 10 = 39.5$

㉒ $4.08 \bigcirc 100 = 408$

㉓ $880 \bigcirc 1000 = 0.88$

㉔ $2.6 \bigcirc 10 = 0.26$

㉕ $14.5 \bigcirc 10 = 1.45$

㉖ $0.56 \bigcirc 100 = 56$

㉗ $27.8 \bigcirc 1000 = 27\ 800$

㉘ $1.37 \bigcirc 100 = 137$

Mark Tim and Kim's work. If an answer is correct, put a check mark; otherwise, cross it out and write the correct answer above it. Then answer the question.

㉙

Name: Tim

1. $0.38 \times \underline{\ 100\ } = 38$

2. $718 \div \underline{\ 10\ } = 71.8$

3. $6.02 \times \underline{\ 100\ } = 6020$

4. $29.9 \div \underline{\ 100\ } = 2.99$

5. $405 \div \underline{\ 100\ } = 4.05$

6. $1.28 \times \underline{\ 1000\ } = 12.8$

Name: Kim

1. $6.1 \div \underline{\ 10\ } = 0.61$

2. $5.89 \times \underline{\ 10\ } = 58.9$

3. $0.08 \times \underline{\ 1000\ } = 80$

4. $890 \div \underline{\ 1000\ } = 0.89$

5. $3.5 \times \underline{\ 100\ } = 3500$

6. $465 \div \underline{\ 10\ } = 4.65$

Who got more answers correct?

_____

Find the answers. Show your steps.

③⓪ $0.03 \times 100 \div 10$

     = _____ ÷ 10

     = _____

③① $4500 \div 10 \div 10$

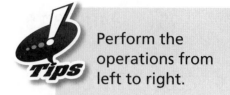

Perform the operations from left to right.

③② $2.8 \times 100 \div 10$

③③ $47.5 \div 10 \times 1000$

③④ $285 \div 100 \times 100$

③⑤ $60.3 \times 1000 \div 100$

③⑥ $109.5 \div 10 \times 100$

③⑦ $14.75 \times 100 \div 10$

③⑧ $32.4 \times 1000 \div 1000$

③⑨ $198.4 \div 10 \times 100$

④⓪ $24.9 \times 10 \div 1000$

Find the answers mentally.

④① $0.6 \times 1000 \div 10$ = _____

④② $24.9 \times 10 \div 100$ = _____

④③ $9.28 \div 100 \times 10$ = _____

④④ $5.07 \times 100 \div 1000$ = _____

④⑤ $0.02 \div 10 \times 1000$ = _____

④⑥ $45 \div 1000 \times 100$ = _____

Move the decimal point the correct number of places and in the correct direction to figure out the answers.

For each train, cross out the coach that does not have the given answer.

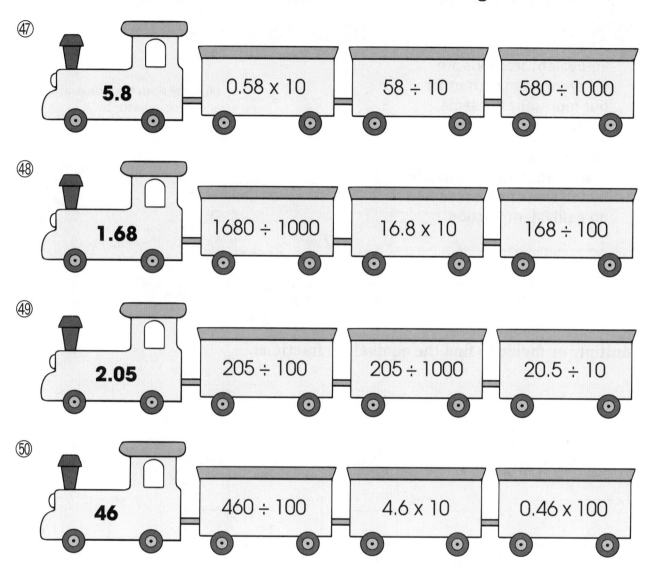

47 **5.8** | 0.58 x 10 | 58 ÷ 10 | 580 ÷ 1000

48 **1.68** | 1680 ÷ 1000 | 16.8 x 10 | 168 ÷ 100

49 **2.05** | 205 ÷ 100 | 205 ÷ 1000 | 20.5 ÷ 10

50 **46** | 460 ÷ 100 | 4.6 x 10 | 0.46 x 100

Fill in the blanks.

51 Multiplying a number by _____ moves the decimal point 3 places to the _____ .

52 When a number is divided by 10, 100, or 1000, the answer will be _____ than the number.

53 _____ a number by 10 moves the decimal point _____ place(s) to the left.

4 Equivalent Fractions

• finding equivalent fractions

Equivalent fractions are different from each other but represent the same value.

Multiply or divide the numerator and denominator by the same number to find an equivalent fraction.

Example Write an equivalent fraction.

$$\overset{\times 2}{\underset{\times 2}{\frac{1}{3} = \frac{2}{6}}}$$

Multiply both the numerator and denominator by 2.

Try It

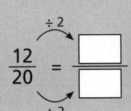

$$\overset{\div 2}{\underset{\div 2}{\frac{12}{20} = \frac{\boxed{}}{\boxed{}}}}$$

Divide both the numerator and denominator by 2.

Multiply or divide to find the equivalent fractions.

① **x 2**

$\dfrac{1}{5} = \dfrac{\boxed{}}{10}$

$\dfrac{3}{4} = \dfrac{6}{\boxed{}}$

② **x 3**

$\dfrac{2}{3} = \dfrac{6}{\boxed{}}$

$\dfrac{3}{7} = \dfrac{\boxed{}}{21}$

③ **÷ 2**

$\dfrac{4}{10} = \dfrac{2}{\boxed{}}$

$\dfrac{12}{14} = \dfrac{\boxed{}}{7}$

④ **÷ 5**

$\dfrac{20}{25} = \dfrac{\boxed{}}{5}$

$\dfrac{15}{50} = \dfrac{3}{\boxed{}}$

⑤ **x 5**

$\dfrac{3}{4} = \dfrac{15}{\boxed{}}$

$\dfrac{1}{3} = \underline{}$

$\dfrac{6}{9} = \underline{}$

⑥ **÷ 3**

$\dfrac{12}{15} = \dfrac{\boxed{}}{5}$

$\dfrac{6}{30} = \underline{}$

$\dfrac{18}{24} = \underline{}$

⑦ **x 4**

$\dfrac{2}{3} = \dfrac{8}{\boxed{}}$

$\dfrac{2}{5} = \underline{}$

$\dfrac{8}{20} = \underline{}$

Find the missing numbers.

⑧
$$\frac{2}{3} = \frac{20}{30}$$
(×) (×)

⑨
$$\frac{24}{32} = \frac{3}{4}$$
(÷) (÷)

⑩
$$\frac{3}{5} = \frac{15}{25}$$
(×) (×)

⑪
$$\frac{35}{42} = \frac{5}{6}$$
(÷) (÷)

⑫
$$\frac{7}{8} = \frac{49}{56}$$
(×) (×)

⑬
$$\frac{36}{63} = \frac{4}{7}$$
(÷) (÷)

⑭
$$\frac{9}{15} = \frac{\boxed{}}{5} = \frac{\boxed{}}{20}$$

⑮
$$\frac{9}{45} = \frac{1}{\boxed{}} = \frac{\boxed{}}{10}$$

⑯
$$\frac{14}{35} = \frac{\boxed{}}{5} = \frac{\boxed{}}{10}$$

⑰
$$\frac{11}{\boxed{}} = \frac{1}{5} = \frac{\boxed{}}{20}$$

⑱
$$\frac{\boxed{}}{24} = \frac{10}{12} = \frac{5}{\boxed{}}$$

⑲
$$\frac{20}{45} = \frac{\boxed{}}{9} = \frac{8}{\boxed{}}$$

Write 3 equivalent fractions for each of the given fractions.

⑳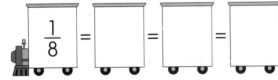
$$\frac{1}{8} = \boxed{} = \boxed{} = \boxed{}$$

㉑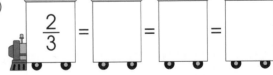
$$\frac{2}{3} = \boxed{} = \boxed{} = \boxed{}$$

㉒
$$\frac{3}{12} = \boxed{} = \boxed{} = \boxed{}$$

㉓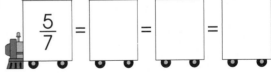
$$\frac{5}{7} = \boxed{} = \boxed{} = \boxed{}$$

㉔
$$\frac{5}{6} = \boxed{} = \boxed{} = \boxed{}$$

㉕
$$\frac{14}{20} = \boxed{} = \boxed{} = \boxed{}$$

Write the fractions in simplest form.

㉖ $\dfrac{20}{30} = \dfrac{\boxed{}}{3}$

㉗ $\dfrac{5}{10} = \dfrac{1}{\boxed{}}$

Hints

When the numerator and denominator of a fraction have no common factors other than 1, that fraction is in its simplest form.

㉘ $\dfrac{21}{28} = \dfrac{3}{\boxed{}}$

㉙ $\dfrac{15}{20} = \dfrac{\boxed{}}{4}$

To put a fraction in simplest form, divide the numerator and denominator by the greatest common factor (GCF).

㉚ $\dfrac{7}{21} = \dfrac{1}{\boxed{}}$

㉛ $\dfrac{9}{18} = \dfrac{\boxed{}}{2}$

e.g. $\dfrac{12}{20}$ — not in simplest form; common factors: 1, 2, and 4

㉜ $\dfrac{12}{18} = \underline{}$

㉝ $\dfrac{6}{16} = \underline{}$

So,

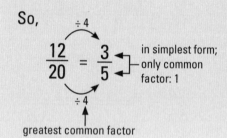

㉞ $\dfrac{12}{15} = \underline{}$

㉟ $\dfrac{25}{30} = \underline{}$

greatest common factor

㊱ $\dfrac{19}{38} = \underline{}$

㊲ $\dfrac{22}{121} = \underline{}$

㊳ $\dfrac{36}{84} = \underline{}$

㊴ $\dfrac{25}{100} = \underline{}$

㊵ $\dfrac{32}{48} = \underline{}$

㊶ $\dfrac{28}{49} = \underline{}$

Match each fraction with its simplest form. Write the letter.

㊷

$\bigcirc$ $\dfrac{10}{12}$　　$\bigcirc$ $\dfrac{18}{21}$　　$\bigcirc$ $\dfrac{3}{15}$

Ⓐ $\dfrac{2}{3}$　　Ⓑ $\dfrac{1}{5}$

Ⓒ $\dfrac{3}{4}$　　Ⓓ $\dfrac{3}{5}$

$\bigcirc$ $\dfrac{6}{8}$　　$\bigcirc$ $\dfrac{6}{10}$　　$\bigcirc$ $\dfrac{6}{9}$

Ⓔ $\dfrac{5}{6}$　　Ⓕ $\dfrac{6}{7}$

Put a check mark on the line if the fraction is in simplest form; otherwise, write it in simplest form.

Fractions in Simplest Form

Tips Follow the steps to write improper fractions as fractions in simplest form.

❶ Rewrite the improper fraction as a mixed number.

❷ Simplify the proper fraction part in the mixed number by using division to find an equivalent fraction.

e.g. $\dfrac{10}{8} = 1\dfrac{2}{8} = 1\dfrac{1}{4}$

in simplest form ⟶

㊸ $\dfrac{10}{3}$ _____

㊹ $1\dfrac{2}{4}$ _____

㊺ $2\dfrac{3}{5}$ _____

㊻ $\dfrac{16}{7}$ _____

㊼ $\dfrac{13}{3}$ _____

㊽ $\dfrac{9}{15}$ _____

㊾ $1\dfrac{15}{10}$ _____

㊿ $\dfrac{20}{6}$ _____

(51) $\dfrac{18}{15}$ _____

(52) $2\dfrac{8}{9}$ _____

(53) $\dfrac{12}{4}$ _____

(54) $1\dfrac{4}{5}$ _____

(55) $3\dfrac{2}{6}$ _____

(56) $5\dfrac{1}{3}$ _____

(57) $2\dfrac{6}{5}$ _____

(58) $1\dfrac{8}{10}$ _____

Look at each group of fractions. Cross out the one that is not equivalent to the rest. Circle the one in simplest form.

(59)
$\dfrac{5}{2}$ $1\dfrac{4}{8}$
     $\dfrac{6}{4}$
$1\dfrac{1}{2}$ $\dfrac{9}{6}$

(60)
$1\dfrac{8}{5}$ $\dfrac{23}{10}$
     $\dfrac{13}{5}$
$2\dfrac{3}{5}$ $1\dfrac{16}{10}$

(61)
$2\dfrac{7}{3}$ $1\dfrac{14}{6}$
     $2\dfrac{12}{9}$
$3\dfrac{1}{3}$ $\dfrac{20}{6}$

5 Ordering Fractions

- comparing and ordering fractions

Follow the steps to compare fractions.

❶ Find equivalent fractions that have the same denominator.

❷ Compare their numerators. The one with the greater numerator is the greater fraction.

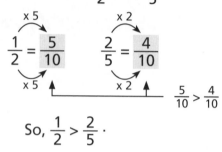

Example Compare $\frac{1}{2}$ and $\frac{2}{5}$.

$$\overset{\times 5}{\frac{1}{2} = \frac{5}{10}} \quad \overset{\times 2}{\frac{2}{5} = \frac{4}{10}}$$

$$\underset{\times 5}{} \qquad \underset{\times 2}{} \qquad \frac{5}{10} > \frac{4}{10}$$

So, $\frac{1}{2} > \frac{2}{5}$.

Try It

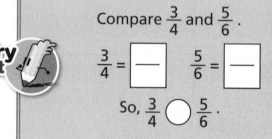

Compare $\frac{3}{4}$ and $\frac{5}{6}$.

$$\frac{3}{4} = \boxed{} \qquad \frac{5}{6} = \boxed{}$$

So, $\frac{3}{4} \bigcirc \frac{5}{6}$.

Compare the fractions. Write "<", ">", or "=".

①
a. $\frac{2}{3} \bigcirc \frac{3}{4}$

b. $\frac{1}{5} \bigcirc \frac{1}{2}$

c. $\frac{4}{6} \bigcirc \frac{2}{3}$

d. $\frac{3}{4} \bigcirc \frac{5}{8}$

e. $\frac{1}{4} \bigcirc \frac{2}{9}$

f. $\frac{2}{5} \bigcirc \frac{1}{3}$

g. $\frac{7}{10} \bigcirc \frac{2}{3}$

②
a. $\frac{10}{6} \bigcirc \frac{4}{3}$

b. $\frac{14}{6} \bigcirc \frac{18}{8}$

c. $\frac{5}{3} \bigcirc \frac{3}{2}$

d. $\frac{11}{3} \bigcirc \frac{9}{2}$

e. $\frac{7}{5} \bigcirc \frac{10}{7}$

f. $\frac{20}{8} \bigcirc \frac{15}{6}$

g. $\frac{16}{5} \bigcirc \frac{14}{3}$

③
a. $1\frac{3}{4} \bigcirc 1\frac{1}{2}$

b. $1\frac{2}{7} \bigcirc 1\frac{4}{9}$

c. $1\frac{2}{3} \bigcirc 1\frac{4}{6}$

d. $2\frac{4}{9} \bigcirc 4\frac{2}{9}$

e. $1\frac{2}{3} \bigcirc 2\frac{1}{5}$

f. $2\frac{1}{5} \bigcirc 2\frac{1}{4}$

g. $3\frac{5}{6} \bigcirc 3\frac{5}{8}$

Write each fraction in its simplest form. Then put the fractions in order from smallest to greatest.

④ $\dfrac{5}{25}$ $\dfrac{6}{15}$ $\dfrac{8}{10}$ $\dfrac{12}{20}$ $\dfrac{5}{25} <$ _____ $<$ _____ $<$ _____

⑤ $\dfrac{6}{18}$ $\dfrac{2}{12}$ $\dfrac{12}{24}$ $\dfrac{25}{30}$ _____

⑥ $\dfrac{10}{16}$ $\dfrac{15}{30}$ $\dfrac{21}{24}$ $\dfrac{15}{20}$ _____

⑦ $\dfrac{21}{30}$ $\dfrac{20}{25}$ $\dfrac{11}{22}$ $\dfrac{27}{45}$ _____

Put the improper fractions and mixed numbers in order.

⑧ $2\dfrac{1}{5}$ $\dfrac{13}{5}$ $\dfrac{9}{5}$ _____ $<$ _____ $<$ _____

⑨ $\dfrac{6}{4}$ $1\dfrac{3}{4}$ $\dfrac{10}{4}$ _____ $<$ _____ $<$ _____

⑩ $\dfrac{13}{7}$ $1\dfrac{4}{7}$ $\dfrac{10}{7}$ _____ $<$ _____ $<$ _____

⑪ $\dfrac{7}{3}$ $1\dfrac{2}{3}$ $\dfrac{4}{3}$ _____ $<$ _____ $<$ _____

 Tips It is easier to compare fractions if they are all in the form of either improper fractions or mixed numbers.

⑫ $\dfrac{17}{6}$ $3\dfrac{4}{6}$ $\dfrac{20}{6}$ $3\dfrac{1}{6}$

_____ $>$ _____ $>$ _____ $>$ _____

⑬ $2\dfrac{3}{8}$ $\dfrac{21}{8}$ $\dfrac{18}{8}$ $2\dfrac{7}{8}$

_____ $>$ _____ $>$ _____ $>$ _____

Put the fractions in order from smallest to greatest.

⑭ $\dfrac{2}{3}$ $1\dfrac{1}{3}$ $\dfrac{5}{3}$ $\dfrac{1}{3}$

_____

Tips

A proper fraction is always smaller than an improper fraction or a mixed number.

⑮ $1\dfrac{1}{7}$ $\dfrac{6}{7}$ $\dfrac{9}{7}$ $1\dfrac{3}{7}$

_____

⑯ $\dfrac{9}{8}$ $1\dfrac{3}{8}$ $\dfrac{10}{8}$ $\dfrac{7}{8}$ $1\dfrac{5}{8}$

_____

⑰ $\dfrac{5}{3}$ $2\dfrac{2}{3}$ $\dfrac{9}{3}$ $\dfrac{7}{3}$ $\dfrac{15}{3}$

_____

⑱ $\dfrac{11}{4}$ $1\dfrac{3}{4}$ $\dfrac{17}{4}$ $2\dfrac{1}{4}$ $\dfrac{16}{4}$

_____

For each set, circle the smallest and greatest fractions with the specified colours.

⑲

 red   **smallest fraction**   blue   **greatest fraction**

a.
$\dfrac{4}{7}$ $\dfrac{8}{7}$

$1\dfrac{2}{7}$ $\dfrac{3}{7}$

b.
$1\dfrac{8}{9}$ $\dfrac{11}{9}$

$\dfrac{7}{9}$ $2\dfrac{1}{9}$

c.
$\dfrac{20}{6}$ $3\dfrac{1}{6}$

$1\dfrac{5}{6}$ $\dfrac{17}{6}$

d.
$2\dfrac{1}{8}$ $1\dfrac{1}{8}$

$\dfrac{10}{8}$ $\dfrac{13}{8}$

Write a fraction for each description.

⑳ Write a proper fraction that is

    a. smaller than $\frac{4}{7}$.

                                                                  b. between $\frac{2}{5}$ and $1\frac{3}{5}$.

_____   _____

㉑ Write an improper fraction that is

    a. greater than $\frac{1}{9}$.

                                                                   b. between $1\frac{1}{6}$ and $1\frac{5}{6}$.

_____   _____

㉒ Write a mixed number that is

    a. greater than $2\frac{1}{3}$.

                                                                  b. between $1\frac{2}{9}$ and $2\frac{1}{9}$.

_____   _____

Colour each diagram to show a fraction that matches the given description. Then write the fraction.

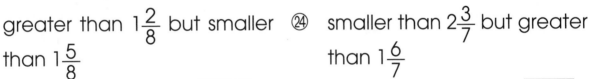

㉓ greater than $1\frac{2}{8}$ but smaller than $1\frac{5}{8}$

㉔ smaller than $2\frac{3}{7}$ but greater than $1\frac{6}{7}$

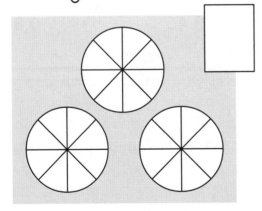
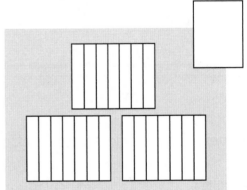

㉕ greater than 1 but smaller than $\frac{15}{6}$

6 Fractions and Decimals

- converting fractions and decimals

Read This

Follow the steps to convert a decimal into a fraction.

1. Write the decimal number as a numerator and drop the decimal point.

2. To find the denominator, count the number of decimal places in the decimal. Write 10 for 1 decimal place, 100 for 2 decimal places, and so on.

3. Reduce to simplest form.

Example Convert the decimals into fractions.

$$0.7 = \frac{7}{10}$$ ← 7 as the numerator
← 10 for 1 decimal place

1 decimal place

$$0.55 = \frac{55}{100}$$ ← 55 as the numerator
← 100 for 2 decimal places

2 decimal places

$$= \frac{11}{20}$$ ← in simplest form

Try It

$0.3 = \boxed{}$ $0.85 = \boxed{}$

Circle the correct fraction for each decimal.

① **0.3**

$\frac{3}{10}$ $\frac{1}{3}$

② **0.9**

$\frac{9}{100}$ $\frac{9}{10}$

③ **0.31**

$\frac{31}{100}$ $3\frac{1}{10}$

④ **0.09**

$\frac{9}{100}$ $\frac{3}{10}$

⑤ **0.7**

$\frac{7}{10}$ $\frac{7}{1}$

⑥ **0.1**

$\frac{1}{10}$ $1\frac{1}{10}$

⑦ **0.45**

$\frac{45}{10}$ $\frac{9}{20}$

⑧ **0.88**

$\frac{22}{25}$ $\frac{8}{10}$

Convert the decimals into fractions. Write your answers in simplest form.

⑨ 0.01 _____   ⑩ 0.25 _____   ⑪ 0.11 _____   ⑫ 0.5 _____

⑬ 0.2 _____   ⑭ 0.53 _____   ⑮ 0.05 _____   ⑯ 0.08 _____

⑰ 0.16 _____   ⑱ 0.4 _____   ⑲ 0.65 _____   ⑳ 0.94 _____

Write each fraction as a decimal.

㉑ $\dfrac{7}{10}$ = _____

㉒ $\dfrac{3}{100}$ = _____

$\dfrac{1}{10} = 0.1$

㉓ $\dfrac{49}{100}$ = _____

㉔ $\dfrac{9}{100}$ = _____

$\dfrac{1}{100} = 0.01$

㉕ $\dfrac{73}{100}$ = _____

㉖ $\dfrac{87}{100}$ = _____

$\dfrac{1}{1000} = 0.001$

㉗ $\dfrac{99}{100}$ = _____

㉘ $\dfrac{3}{1000}$ = _____

㉙ $\dfrac{13}{1000}$ = _____

㉚ $\dfrac{467}{1000}$ = _____

㉛ $\dfrac{87}{1000}$ = _____

㉜ $\dfrac{159}{1000}$ = _____

For each fraction, write an equivalent fraction with a denominator of 10, 100, or 1000. Then convert it into a decimal.

㉝ $\dfrac{1}{2}$ = _____ = _____

㉞ $\dfrac{1}{5}$ = _____ = _____

Hints

㉟ $\dfrac{3}{4}$ = _____ = _____

㊱ $\dfrac{3}{5}$ = _____ = _____

Steps to convert a fraction into a decimal:

㊲ $\dfrac{1}{8}$ = _____ = _____

㊳ $\dfrac{5}{8}$ = _____ = _____

❶ Find the equivalent fraction with a denominator of 10, 100, 1000, etc.

㊴ $\dfrac{3}{8}$ = _____ = _____

㊵ $\dfrac{4}{5}$ = _____ = _____

❷ Write the equivalent fraction as a decimal.

㊶ $\dfrac{7}{25}$ = _____ = _____

㊷ $\dfrac{29}{50}$ = _____ = _____

e.g. $\dfrac{1}{4} = \dfrac{25}{100} = 0.25$

㊸ $\dfrac{499}{500}$ = _____ = _____

㊹ $\dfrac{9}{125}$ = _____ = _____

㊺ $\dfrac{143}{250}$ = _____ = _____

Do the conversions. Write the fractions in simplest form.

46 Decimals ➡ Fractions

a. 0.65 _____

b. 0.75 _____

c. 0.36 _____

d. 1.2 _____

e. 1.5 _____

f. 2.15 _____

g. 1.01 _____

h. 2.75 _____

47 Fractions ➡ Decimals

a. $\frac{1}{4}$ _____

b. $\frac{17}{20}$ _____

c. $\frac{19}{25}$ _____

d. $1\frac{1}{8}$ _____

e. $1\frac{2}{5}$ _____

f. $2\frac{4}{5}$ _____

g. $3\frac{1}{2}$ _____

h. $2\frac{1}{4}$ _____

Find how many cents each child has. Colour the child with the most money.

48  $\$\frac{1}{4} = \$\underline{\hspace{1cm}}_{\text{decimal}} = \underline{\hspace{1cm}}_{\substack{\text{whole}\\\text{number}}}$ ¢

49 $\$\frac{2}{5} = \$\underline{\hspace{1cm}} = \underline{\hspace{1cm}}$ ¢

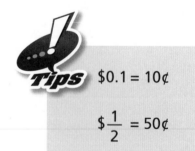
Tips $0.1 = 10¢

$\$\frac{1}{2} = 50¢$

50 $\$\frac{3}{4} = \$\underline{\hspace{1cm}} = \underline{\hspace{1cm}}$ ¢

51 $\$\frac{3}{5} = \$\underline{\hspace{1cm}} = \underline{\hspace{1cm}}$ ¢

52 $\$\frac{7}{10} = \$\underline{\hspace{1cm}} = \underline{\hspace{1cm}}$ ¢

53 $\$\frac{9}{10} = \$\underline{\hspace{1cm}} = \underline{\hspace{1cm}}$ ¢

Circle the greater number in each pair.

54 0.65 $\dfrac{1}{2}$

55 $\dfrac{4}{5}$ 0.9

56 1.3 $1\dfrac{2}{5}$

57 $\dfrac{2}{3}$ 0.62

58 4.26 $4\dfrac{1}{4}$

59 0.57 $\dfrac{8}{15}$

60 3.69 $3\dfrac{3}{5}$

61 8.38 $8\dfrac{1}{3}$

62 $6\dfrac{3}{8}$ 6.37

Write the numbers in order from smallest to greatest.

63 $1\dfrac{7}{8}$ 1.54 $1\dfrac{8}{9}$ _____ < _____ < _____

64 2.68 $2\dfrac{3}{5}$ $2\dfrac{4}{7}$ _____

65 $5\dfrac{9}{10}$ $5\dfrac{4}{5}$ 5.83   _____

Complete the tables. Then put the fractions in the specified order.

66 a.

Fraction	$\dfrac{1}{8}$	$\dfrac{1}{4}$	$\dfrac{3}{4}$	$\dfrac{3}{8}$	$\dfrac{7}{8}$	$\dfrac{1}{5}$
Decimal						

b. Put the fractions in order from smallest to greatest.

_____ < _____ < _____ < _____ < _____

67 a.

Decimal	0.6	0.85	0.54	0.36	0.75	1.5
Fraction (in simplest form)						

b. Put the fractions in order from greatest to smallest.

_____ > _____ > _____ > _____ > _____

7 Money

- writing and adding money amounts

It is easier to find money amounts when the bills and coins are sorted by value and counted from the ones with the highest value to the lowest.

Example Write the money amounts.

Bill/Coin	No.	Subtotal
$50	3	$150
$20	2	$40
$2	3	$6
	Total:	$196

Try It

Bill/Coin	No.	Subtotal
$10		
$5		
$1		
	Total:	

Find the money amounts.

①

Bill/Coin	No.	Subtotal
	Total:	

②

Bill/Coin	No.	Subtotal
	Total:	

Draw bills and coins to show the given money amounts in two ways.

③

With the fewest bills and coins

Another way

④

With the fewest bills and coins

Another way

⑤

With the fewest bills and coins

Another way

Colour the correct number of bills and coins needed to buy each item.

⑥

$46.55

| $10 | $5 |

25¢   5¢   10¢

| $10 | $5 |

$1   25¢   10¢

10¢ | $20 |

⑦

$72.45

| $50 | $10 |

10¢ $2

10¢

| $20 |

$20

5¢   10¢

| $10 | 25¢   25¢

⑧

$118.20

| $100 | $5 |

$1 $1   10¢

$2 | $5 | | $50 |

| $20 | $2   10¢   10¢

| $10 | 25¢   10¢

⑨

$234.65

| $5 | $2 $1

| $100 |

| $10 | $1 $2

| $100 | 25¢   25¢   25¢

| $20 | 10¢   5¢

| $50 | 10¢

Write the money amount that each child has. Check the most expensive item that each child can afford.

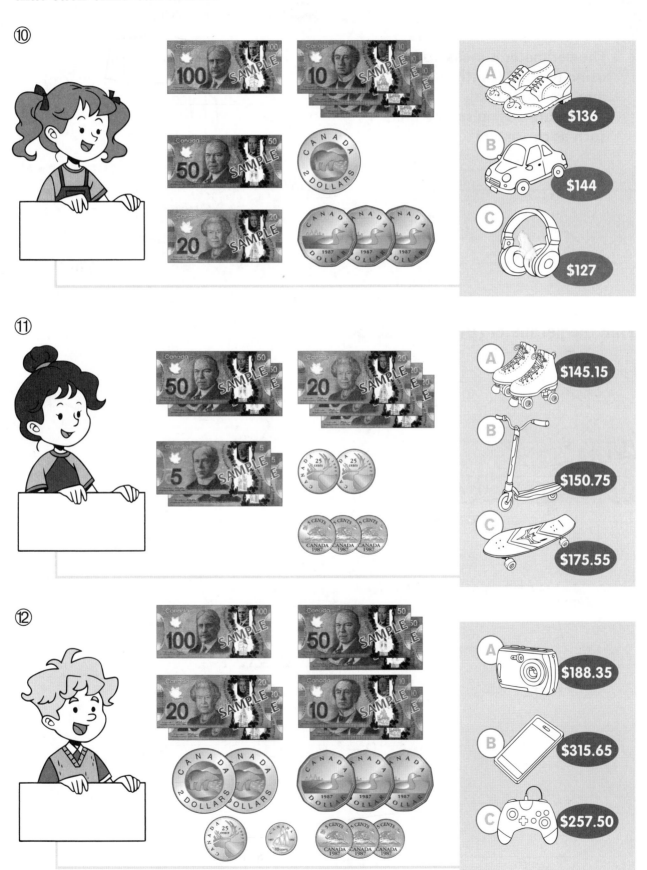

⑩
A $136
B $144
C $127

⑪
A $145.15
B $150.75
C $175.55

⑫
A $188.35
B $315.65
C $257.50

Perimeter and Area

• finding perimeters and areas

Read This

The perimeter is measured using units of length such as mm, cm, m, and km. The area is measured using square units such as cm² and m².

Example Find the perimeter and area.

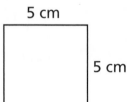

5 cm

5 cm

Perimeter:
4 x 5 = 20 (cm)

Area:
5 x 5 = 25 (cm²)

Try It

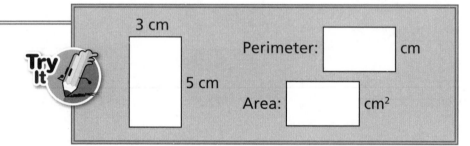

3 cm

5 cm

Perimeter: _____ cm

Area: _____ cm²

Find the perimeter (P) of each shape.

①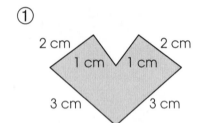

2 cm   2 cm
1 cm   1 cm
3 cm   3 cm

P = _____

②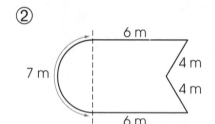

6 m
7 m   4 m
4 m
6 m

P = _____

③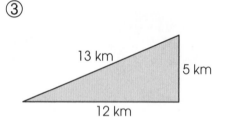

13 km   5 km
12 km

P = _____

④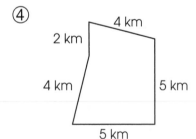

4 km
2 km
4 km   5 km
5 km

P = _____

⑤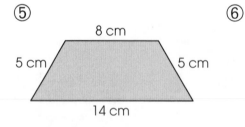

8 cm
5 cm   5 cm
14 cm

P = _____

⑥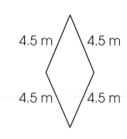

4.5 m   4.5 m
4.5 m   4.5 m

P = _____

⑦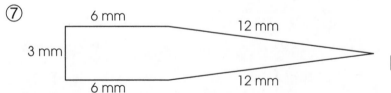

6 mm
12 mm
3 mm
6 mm   12 mm

P = _____

Find the perimeter and area of each shape on the centimetre grid.

⑧

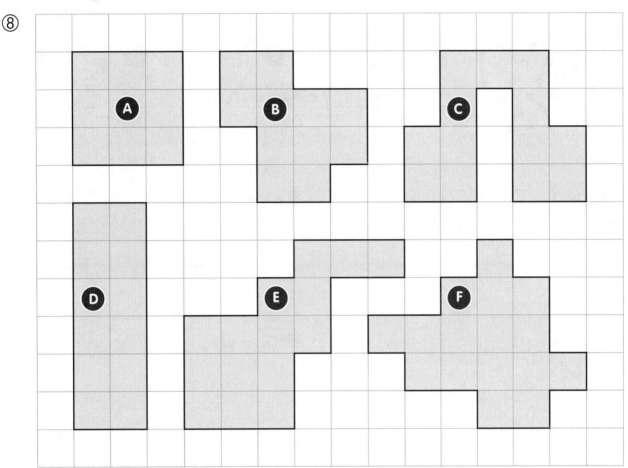

a. **Perimeter   Area**

Ⓐ _____   _____

Ⓑ _____   _____

Ⓒ _____   _____

Ⓓ _____   _____

Ⓔ _____   _____

Ⓕ _____   _____

b. Which shape has the

• smallest perimeter?

_____

• greatest perimeter?

_____

• smallest area?

_____

• greatest area?

_____

LEVEL 2 – FURTHER YOUR UNDERSTANDING

Find the perimeters and areas of the shapes. Then match the descriptions with the shapes.

⑨

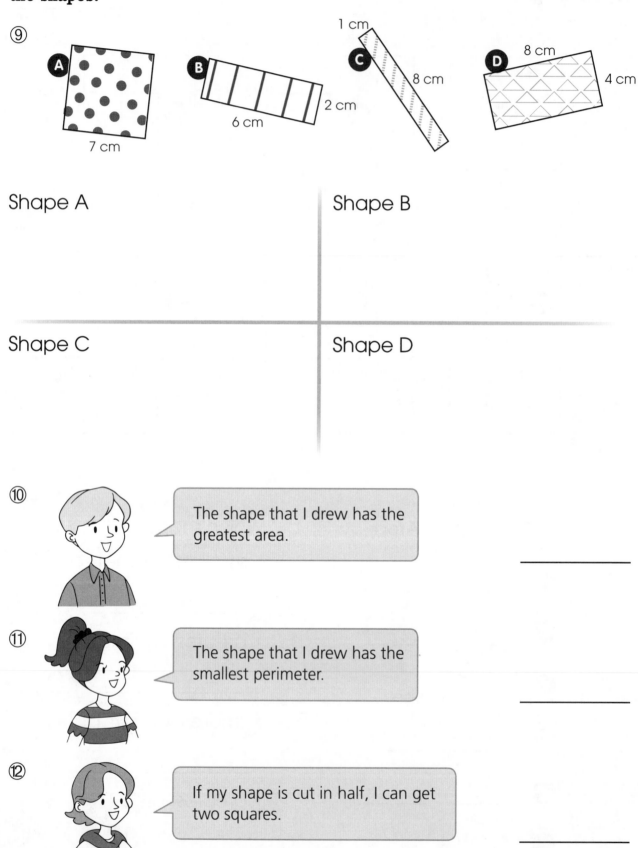

Shape A

Shape B

Shape C

Shape D

⑩ The shape that I drew has the greatest area.

_____

⑪ The shape that I drew has the smallest perimeter.

_____

⑫ If my shape is cut in half, I can get two squares.

_____

Draw the shapes with the given measurements. Then find the perimeters and areas.

⑬
Square
Side length: 4 cm

P: _____   A: _____

⑭
Rectangle
Length: 5 cm Width: 3 cm

P: _____   A: _____

Draw all the possible rectangles and label them.

⑮

Rectangle A
- area of 12 cm²
- perimeter of 14 cm

Rectangle B
- same area as Rectangle A
- greater perimeter than Rectangle A

Rectangle C
- same perimeter as Rectangle A
- smaller area than Rectangle A

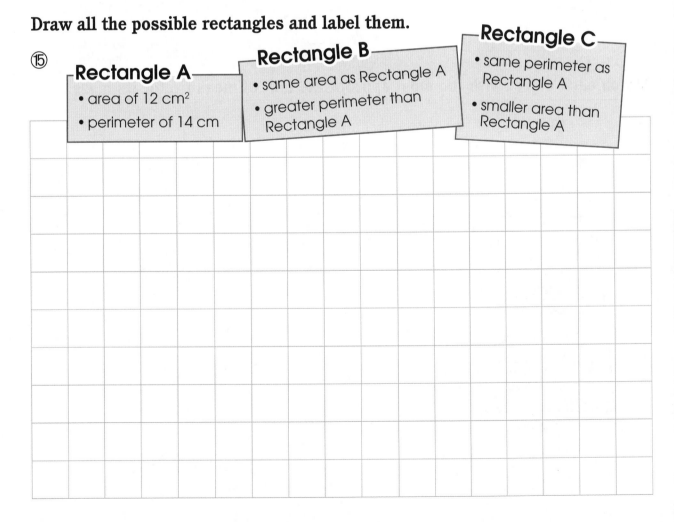

LEVEL 2 – FURTHER YOUR UNDERSTANDING

9 Mass

• measuring masses in milligrams, grams, kilograms, and tonnes

The mass is a measure of how much something weighs. It is measured in milligrams (mg), grams (g), kilograms (kg), and tonnes (t).

small unit
- milligram (mg)
- gram (g)
- kilogram (kg)
big unit
- tonne (t)

Example Write the most appropriate unit of measure for the mass of each animal.

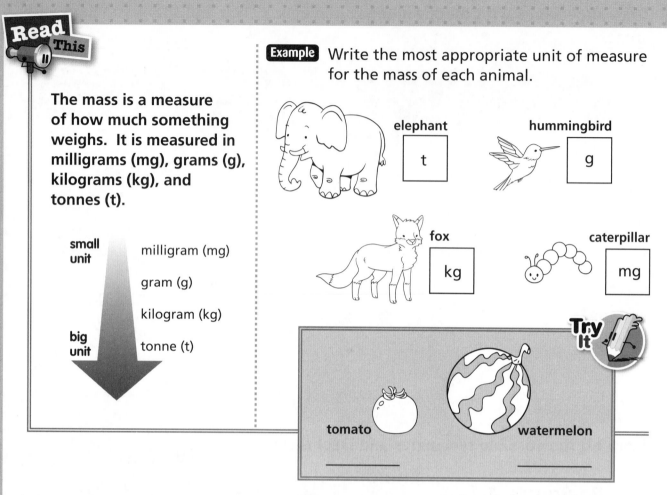

elephant — t

hummingbird — g

fox — kg

caterpillar — mg

Try It

tomato   watermelon

_____   _____

Match each object with the most appropriate unit of measure for its mass.

①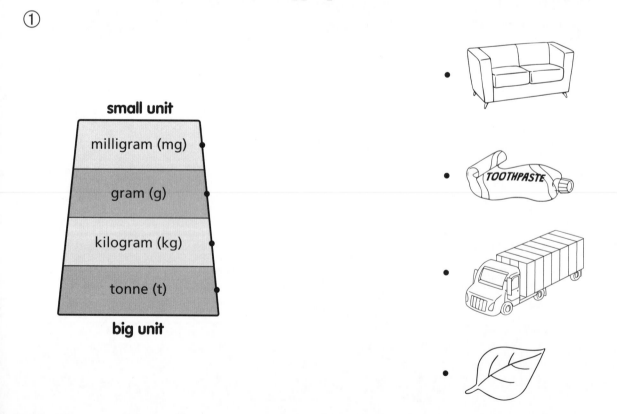

small unit
- milligram (mg)
- gram (g)
- kilogram (kg)
- tonne (t)

big unit

Complete each set of conversions.

② **milligrams and grams**

a. 2 g = _____ mg

b. 5 g = _____ mg

c. 11 g = _____ mg

d. 7000 mg = _____ g

e. 3000 mg = _____ g

f. 4000 mg = _____ g

1 g = 1000 mg

1 kg = 1000 g

1 t = 1000 kg

③ **grams and kilograms**

a. 4 kg = _____ g

b. 2 kg = _____ g

c. 10 kg = _____ g

d. 3000 g = _____ kg

e. 8000 g = _____ kg

f. 5000 g = _____ kg

④ **kilograms and tonnes**

a. 3 t = _____ kg

b. 6 t = _____ kg

c. 9 t = _____ kg

d. 4000 kg = _____ t

e. 2000 kg = _____ t

f. 17 000 kg = _____ t

Do the conversions for each object.

⑤

185 g

_____ mg

_____ kg

_____ t

⑥

0.5 t

_____ mg

_____ g

_____ kg

⑦

125 kg

_____ mg

_____ g

_____ t

Check the heavier item in each pair.

⑧

Ⓐ 9.18 kg   Ⓑ 9250 g

⑨

Ⓐ 125 g   Ⓑ 0.25 kg

⑩

Ⓐ 750 kg   Ⓑ 0.65 t

⑪

Ⓐ 368 g   Ⓑ 375 000 mg

⑫

Ⓐ 7.7 kg   Ⓑ 5000 g

⑬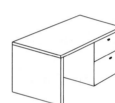

Ⓐ 67 kg   Ⓑ 0.054 t

Sort the objects as specified. Write the letters.

⑭ from lightest to heaviest

Ⓐ    Ⓑ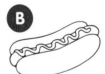

2.1 kg   **120 g**

Ⓒ   Ⓓ

0.36 kg   **250 g**

⑮ from heaviest to lightest

Ⓐ    Ⓑ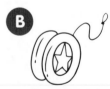

5 g   **6200 mg**

Ⓒ    Ⓓ

4200 mg   **7.2 g**

_____   _____

Find the sum and difference of the masses in each pair in the specified unit.

⑯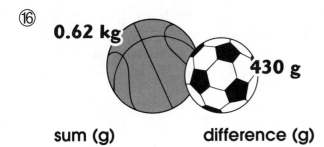

0.62 kg

430 g

sum (g)   difference (g)

⑰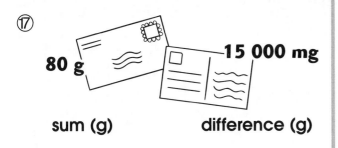

80 g   15 000 mg

sum (g)   difference (g)

⑱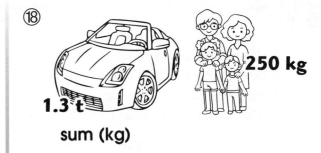

1.3 t   250 kg

sum (kg)

difference (kg)

⑲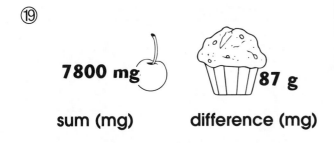

7800 mg   87 g

sum (mg)   difference (mg)

⑳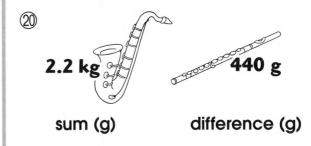

2.2 kg   440 g

sum (g)   difference (g)

10 Transformations

- translating, reflecting, and rotating shapes

Read This

To translate a shape, move every point of the shape the same distance in the same direction(s).

Do not forget that the translated image should have the same size and shape as the original one.

Example Translate the shape 5 units to the right and 1 unit down.

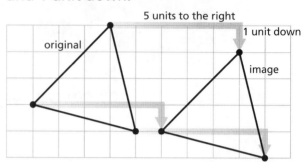

Try It

Translate the shape 4 units to the left and 1 unit up.

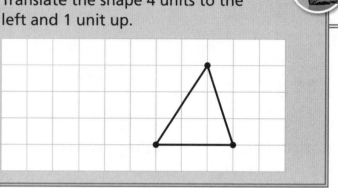

Do the translations.

① Translate each shape 4 units to the right and 3 units up.

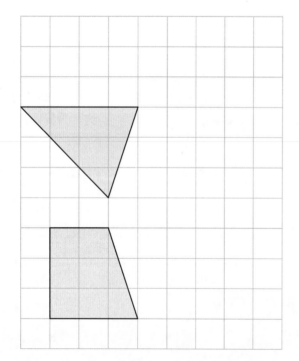

② Translate each shape 2 units to the left and 3 units down.

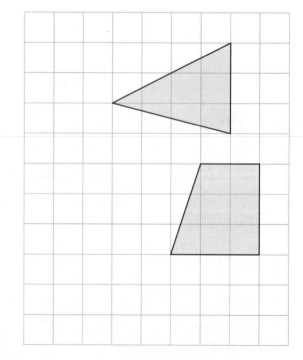

Reflect each shape in the given line of reflection.

③

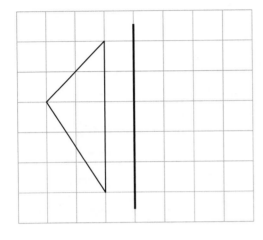

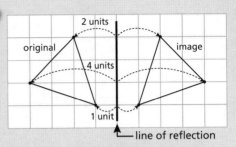

The corresponding vertices are the same distances from the line of reflection.

④

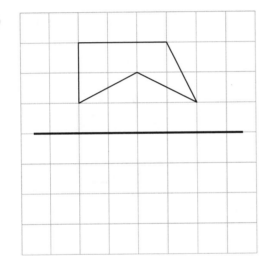

⑤

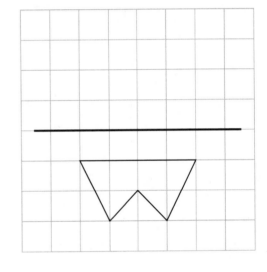

Reflect the shapes as specified.

⑥ Reflect the parallelogram in Line S.

Reflect the trapezoid in Line S.

Reflect the triangle in Line S. Then reflect its image in Line R.

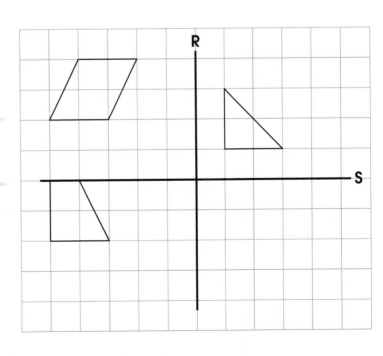

Do the rotations with the given centres of rotation.

⑦ $\frac{1}{2}$ turn

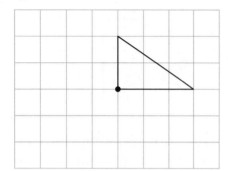

⑧ $\frac{1}{4}$ turn clockwise

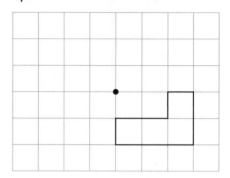

⑨ $\frac{1}{4}$ turn counterclockwise

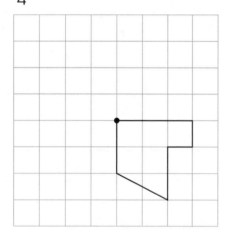

⑩ $\frac{3}{4}$ turn clockwise

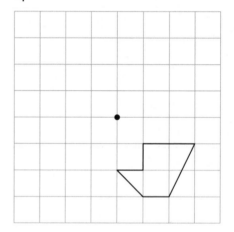

Do the rotations. Then answer the questions.

⑪

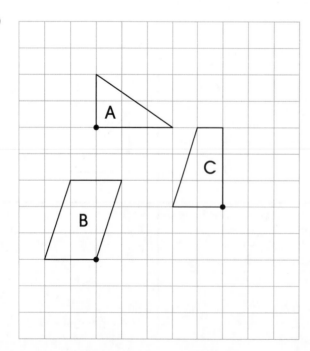

Make a $\frac{1}{4}$ turn counterclockwise with Shape A.

Make a $\frac{1}{4}$ turn clockwise with Shape B.

Make a $\frac{1}{2}$ turn with Shape C. Then make another $\frac{1}{2}$ turn with the image. What do you find?

_____

_____

Do the transformations to complete the picture.

⑫

A reflect vertically in Line K

B translate 7 units to the left and 4 units up

C reflect horizontally in Line L

D translate 6 units to the right

E reflect horizontally in Line L

F rotate $\frac{1}{4}$ clockwise 3 times

G rotate $\frac{1}{4}$ counterclockwise 3 times

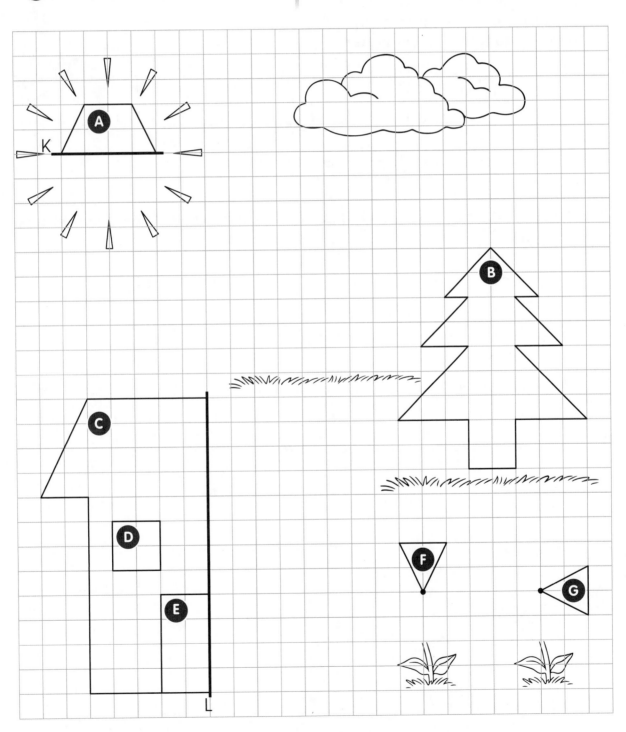

11 Patterning

• representing number patterns

Read This

Geometric patterns are patterns created by shapes. They are classified as "growing" if elements consistently increase, or "shrinking" if elements consistently decrease. Geometric patterns can be represented by numbers to form number patterns.

Example Write as a number pattern.

1 , 3 , 5 , 7 , 9

Try It

10 , _____ , _____ , _____ , _____

Draw the next frame for each pattern. Then write a number pattern to represent it.

①

Number pattern: _____ , _____ , _____ , _____ , _____

②

Number pattern: _____

③

Number pattern: _____

Match each pattern with the correct pattern rule. Then help Monica answer the questions.

④

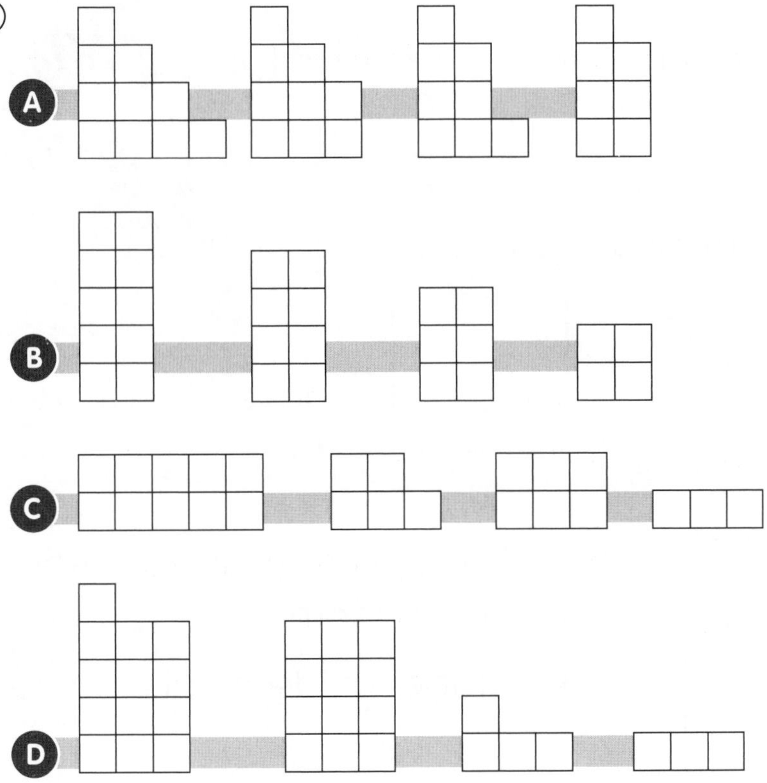

A

B

C

D

Pattern Rule

○ Subtract 1. Then divide by 3.

○ Subtract 1 each time.

○ Subtract 2 each time.

○ Divide by 2. Then add 1.

⑤ *If I extend the patterns, which pattern's next frame will be*

Monica

a. 2 squares? _____

b. 6 squares? _____

c. 4 squares? _____

d. 1 square? _____

⑥ If continued, will Pattern A contain a frame with 4 squares? _____

⑦ Monica has a frame with 3 squares. Which pattern does not contain that frame? _____

Read what the boy says. Draw to help him build the next frame. Then complete the table and answer the questions.

⑧

I'm building triangles using sticks. It takes 3 sticks to build the first triangle.

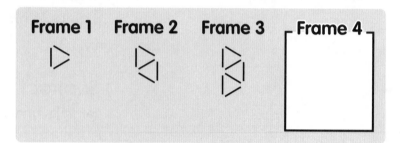

a.

Frame No.	No. of Identical Triangles
1	
2	
3	
4	

Frame No.	No. of Sticks
1	
2	
3	
4	

b. Write a pattern rule to describe each pattern.

• Number of identical triangles:

_____

_____

• Number of sticks:

_____

_____

c. How many identical triangles are there in

• Frame 5? _____   • Frame 7? _____

d. How many sticks are there in

• Frame 5? _____   • Frame 6? _____

e. Which frame has

• 8 triangles? _____   • 15 sticks? _____

Jessie created some patterns. Draw to extend each pattern. Then complete the table and answer the questions.

⑨

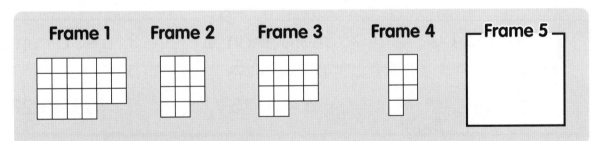

Frame 1 **Frame 2** **Frame 3** **Frame 4** **Frame 5**

a.

Frame No.	No. of Dots
1	
2	
3	
4	
5	

b. Write a pattern rule for the number of dots.

_____

c. How many dots are there in

- Frame 6? _____

- Frame 7? _____

⑩

Frame 1 **Frame 2** **Frame 3** **Frame 4** **Frame 5**

a.

Frame No.	No. of Blocks
1	
2	
3	
4	
5	

b. Write a pattern rule for the number of blocks.

_____

_____

c. How many blocks are there in

- Frame 6? _____

- Frame 8? _____

12 Equations

- writing and solving equations

When there is an unknown number in a problem, use a letter to represent it. Then write the problem as an equation.

Example Check the correct equation.

A number plus 8 is 15.

↑
an unknown

☑ $n + 8 = 15$ ◯ $n - 8 = 15$

Try It

A number subtracted by 5 is 20.

Ⓐ $n - 5 = 20$ Ⓑ $20 - n = 5$

Check the correct equation for each description.

① 4 less than a number is 12.

Ⓐ $b + 4 = 12$

Ⓑ $4 - b = 12$

Ⓒ $b - 4 = 12$

② The sum of 12 and a number is 20.

Ⓐ $s + 20 = 12$

Ⓑ $20 - 12 = s$

Ⓒ $12 + s = 20$

③ The product of w and 5 is 30.

Ⓐ $w \times 5 = 30$

Ⓑ $w \times 30 = 5$

Ⓒ $30 \div 5 = w$

④ 16 divided by z is 8.

Ⓐ $16 \div 8 = z$

Ⓑ $16 \div z = 8$

Ⓒ $8 \div z = 16$

⑤ 6 more than a number is 15.

Ⓐ $6 - y = 15$

Ⓑ $y + 6 = 15$

Ⓒ $y - 6 = 15$

⑥ 3 times a number is 27.

Ⓐ $3 \times p = 27$

Ⓑ $p \div 3 = 27$

Ⓒ $3 \times 27 = p$

Write an equation for each description.

⑦ n divided by 3 is 4.   _____

⑧ 4 more than r is 15.   _____

⑨ k multiplied by 2 is 20.   _____

⑩ 6 subtracted from f is 12.   _____

Write an equation for each. Then use a method of your choice to solve it.

⑪ The sum of 17 and j is 26.

Equation

$j =$ _____

⑫ 11 less than p is 28.

Equation

$p =$ _____

⑬ The product of d and 2 is 20.

Equation

$d =$ _____

⑭ 24 divided by g is 4.

Equation

$g =$ _____

⑮ The product of 8 and y is 64.

Equation

$y =$ _____

⑯ Half of m is 50.

Equation

$m =$ _____

Read each scenario. Check the equation that represents it. Then solve the equation.

⑰

I'm 6 years older than my brother and I'm 15 years old. How old is my brother?

Ⓐ $b - 15 = 6$

Ⓑ $b + 6 = 15$

Answer

_____ years old

⑱

I put all my blocks into stacks of 4. If I have 60 blocks, how many stacks are there?

Ⓐ $4 \times s = 60$

Ⓑ $s \div 4 = 60$

Answer

_____ stacks

⑲

Each pizza is divided into 6 slices. How many pizzas need to be ordered to have 48 slices?

Ⓐ $6 \times p = 48$

Ⓑ $p \div 48 = 6$

Answer

_____ pizzas

⑳

I had 21 bows and then I gave some away. If I have 13 bows left, how many bows did I give away?

Ⓐ $21 - b = 13$

Ⓑ $b - 21 = 13$

Answer

_____ bows

Read each scenario and write an equation to represent it. Then solve it.

I have 14 coins.

Jim and his sister have a total of 33 coins. How many coins does his sister have?

Equation

His sister has _____ coins.

I had 60 pencils.

After giving out some pencils, Ivy has 10 pencils left. How many pencils did she give out?

Equation

She gave out _____ pencils.

I have 45 marbles.

Ali wants to put the marbles equally into boxes so that each box has 9 marbles. How many boxes does she need?

Equation

She needs _____ boxes.

I have 24 comic books.

Ian has 3 times the number of comic books his brother has. How many comic books does Ian's brother have?

Equation

He has _____ comic books.

I had 27 dolls.

Judy donated some of her dolls and has 18 dolls left. How many dolls did she donate?

Equation

She donated _____ dolls.

13 Graphs

- reading graphs and answering questions about them

Graphs are used to display data in an organized way while demonstrating the relationships of the data. Some common graphs include pictographs, bar graphs, line graphs, and circle graphs.

Example Read the circle graph. Check the correct answer.

Beverages Sold

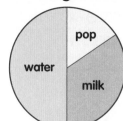

Which beverage is the most popular?

✓ water ← takes up the largest section of the graph

◯ pop

◯ milk

Try It

Which beverage is the least popular?

(A) water   (B) pop   (C) milk

Check the correct answers about each graph.

①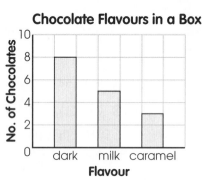

Chocolate Flavours in a Box

a. What type of graph is this?

(A) line graph

(B) bar graph

b. How many flavours are there?

(A) 3

(B) 4

c. How many chocolates are there in the box?

(A) 8

(B) 16

②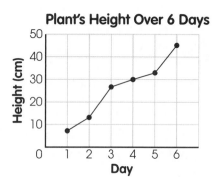

Plant's Height Over 6 Days

a. What type of graph is this?

(A) line graph

(B) bar graph

b. What is the title of the graph?

(A) Plant's Height Over 6 Days

(B) Height (cm) and Day

c. On which day was the plant's height 30 cm?

(A) Day 3

(B) Day 4

Tommy surveyed his friends on their favourite sports and recorded the data in a bar graph. Answer the questions.

My friends chose their favourite sport out of these 7 sports.

③

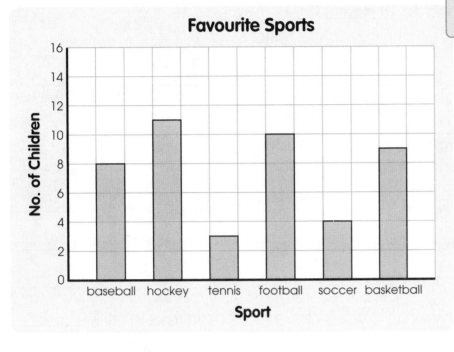

Favourite Sports

a. Which sport is the most popular? _____

b. Which sport is the least popular? _____

c. How many children chose soccer? _____

d. How many children chose football or basketball altogether? _____

e. How many more children chose basketball than tennis? _____

f. How many fewer children chose soccer than football? _____

g. How many sports were chosen by more than 8 children? _____

h. How many children did not choose hockey or soccer? _____

i. How many children were surveyed? _____

The employees at a company were asked what types of vehicles they drive. The results of the survey are shown in the pictograph below.

④

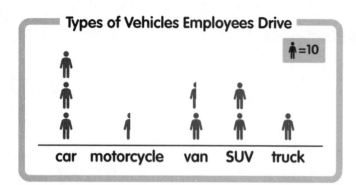

Types of Vehicles Employees Drive

car motorcycle van SUV truck

Tips   ♪ = 5 employees

a. Which type of vehicle is the most common? _____

b. Which type of vehicle is the least common? _____

c. How many employees drive SUVs? _____

d. How many employees drive cars or trucks in all? _____

e. How many employees do not drive vans? _____

f. How many more employees drive cars than motorcycles? _____

g. How many employees were surveyed in all? _____

h. Which type of vehicle makes up $\frac{1}{8}$ of the survey? _____

i. The company uses a circle graph to show the results of the survey. Label each section of the circle graph with the type of vehicle it represents.

Types of Vehicles Employees Drive

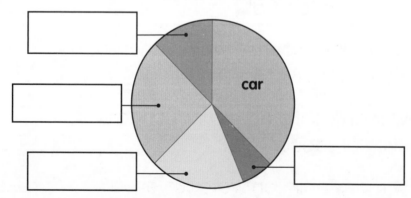

car

The set of data shows the population of Bellfield between 1990 and 2015. Check the correct line graph and answer the questions.

⑤

Year	1990	1995	2000	2005	2010	2015
Population (in thousands)	65	70	78	101	113	130

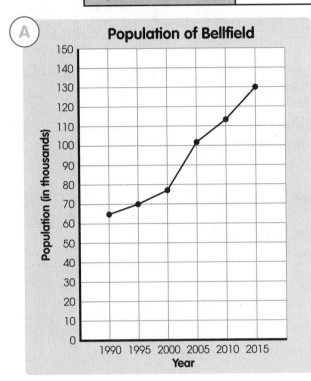

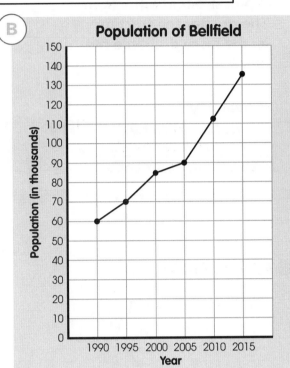

a. What was the population in 1990? _____

b. What was the population in 2015? _____

c. In which year did the population reach 100 000? _____

d. What was the increase in population between 1995 and 2000? _____

e. What was the increase in population between 1995 and 2015? _____

f. During which 5-year period did the population increase the least? _____

g. During which 5-year period did the population increase the most? _____

14 Probability

- finding probabilities

The probability can be represented as a fraction. The greater the fraction is, the more probable the event is.

Probability:

$$\frac{\text{No. of outcomes of a particular event}}{\text{Total no. of outcomes}}$$

Example A card is picked randomly. Find the probability of picking a "4".

| 1 | 2 | 2 | 3 | 3 | 4 |

Probability: $\frac{1}{6}$ ← no. of outcomes with "4"
← total no. of outcomes

Try It Find the probability of picking

- a "1": _____
- a "2": _____

Find the probabilities.

① A dice is tossed.

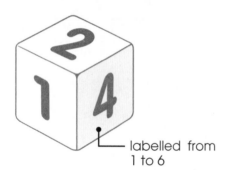

labelled from 1 to 6

What is the probability of getting

a. "2"? _____

b. "4"? _____

c. "3"? _____

d. "8"? _____

e. an odd number? _____

② The wheel is spun.

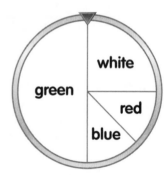

What is the probability of spinning

a. red? _____

b. green? _____

c. black? _____

d. white? _____

e. red or blue? _____

③

| 6 ♠ | 2 ♥ | A ♦ | 6 ♥ | K ♣ | 6 ♦ | 2 ♦ | K ♥ | 2 ♣ | 8 ♦ | 6 ♣ | 8 ♥ |

What is the probability of drawing

a. an "A"? _____ b. a "2"? _____

c. a "6"? _____ d. a "♠"? _____

e. a "♥"? _____ f. a number? _____

g. a letter? _____ h. a "2" with a "♦"? _____

i. a "B" with a "♣"? _____ j. a number with a "♥"? _____

Check the correct tree diagram. Then find the probabilities.

④ Laura tossed a coin and a dice.

a. Which tree diagram shows all the possible outcomes?

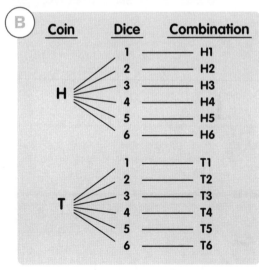

b. What is the probability of getting

• heads and "5"? _____ • tails and "6"? _____

• heads? _____ • a number? _____

• "3"? _____ • heads and an odd number? _____

Complete the tree diagram for the scenario. Then find the probabilities.

⑤ Jo has 2 tops: 1 red and 1 yellow. She also has 2 skirts: 1 blue and 1 grey. Draw a tree diagram to show all the possible outfits.

Top	Skirt	Outfit

a. How many possible outfits are there? _____

b. If she picks an outfit randomly, what is the probability that she picks the clothing below?

- red top and blue skirt _____

- yellow top _____

- yellow top and red skirt _____

Read what Sam says and complete the table. Then find the probabilities.

⑥

I roll two dice. Then I find the sum of the two numbers rolled.

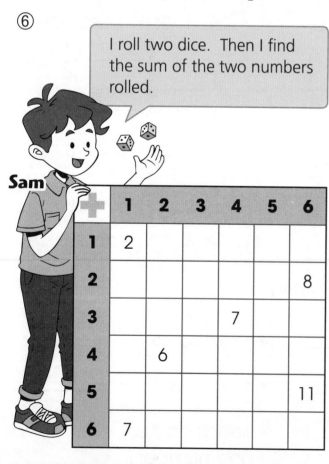

Sam

+	1	2	3	4	5	6
1	2					
2						8
3				7		
4		6				
5						11
6	7					

a. How many possible outcomes are there? _____

b. What is the probability that Sam will get a sum that is

- 2? _____

- 4? _____

- 10? _____

- an even number? _____

- an odd number? _____

- greater than 6? _____

- less than 5? _____

Read what the children say. Then do the colouring and find the probabilities.

⑦

The 8 balls in the box are either red, blue, or green. The probability of picking a red ball is $\frac{1}{4}$, which is equally likely as picking a blue ball.

Probability of picking a

a. blue ball: _____

b. green ball: _____

c. yellow ball: _____

⑧

I have a deck of 7 cards that are red, blue, or green. The probability of picking a green card is $\frac{3}{7}$. It is equally likely to pick a red card and a blue card.

Probability of picking a

a. red card: _____

b. blue card: _____

c. card that is not green: _____

⑨

The spinner has 8 sections that are either red, blue, green, or yellow. It is equally likely to get red and blue. The probabilities of getting green and yellow are the same. The probability of getting red is $\frac{3}{8}$.

Probability of getting

a. blue: _____

b. green: _____

c. yellow: _____

d. not red: _____

e. not green: _____

f. blue or green: _____

LEVEL 3
APPLICATIONS

1 Operations with Whole Numbers (1)

• multiplying and dividing whole numbers

Try It

Alan has 2419 beads. Leo has 12 bags of 55 beads. How many beads do they have in all?

Leo's beads: _____ x _____ = _____

Total beads: _____ + _____ = _____

They have _____ beads in all.

Read This

Steps to solve word problems:

❶ Read the problem thoroughly to identify what you need to answer.

❷ Draw pictures if needed.

❸ Choose the correct operation(s) to solve it step-by-step.

Sally is an antique coin collector. Read about the coins in her collection. Then solve the problems. Show your work.

① Sally is told that her pennies are worth 11¢ each. What is the total value of Sally's pennies?

_____

② Sally is told that her nickels are worth 135¢. How much is each nickel worth?

_____

③ If her dimes are worth 14¢ each, what is the total value of her dimes?

_____

④ Sally has 5 valuable quarters which are worth 116¢ each. The rest are worth 76¢ each. What is the total value of her quarters?

_____

I love collecting old coins.

Sally's Collection

34 pennies
9 nickels
31 dimes
19 quarters

coins

Allan is taking stock of the items in his kitchen. Read what he says and solve the problems. Show your work.

⑤

I have 942 g of raisins, 896 g of peanuts, 14 bags of 63 figs each, 15 bags of 32 apricots each, and 486 cookies.

a. Allan divides his raisins into 6 bags. How many grams of raisins are there in each bag?

_____

b. Allan divides his peanuts into 8 piles. How many grams of peanuts are there in each pile?

_____

c. If each fig weighs 15 g, how much does each bag of figs weigh?

_____

d. If Allan shares his cookies equally with 5 friends, how many cookies does each person get?

_____

e. Allan wants to divide his cookies into bags of 5 or bags of 7. Which way will result in more cookies left over?

_____

f. If Allan puts all his peanuts in 25-g bags, how many bags does he need?

_____

g. If Allan divides the apricots into 5 bags, how many apricots will there be in each bag?

_____

Solve the problems. Show your work.

⑥

A box can hold 9 books and I have 648 books.

a. How many boxes does the boy need?

_____

b. If each box costs $11, how much will the boxes cost in all?

_____

⑦ Peter planted 108 pansies in rows of 9.

a. How many rows of pansies are there?

_____

b. If each row of pansies requires 15 g of fertilizer, how much fertilizer do the pansies need in all?

_____

⑧ Frank puts 448 marbles equally in 8 bags. If each marble weighs 12 g, what is the total weight of the marbles in each bag?

_____

⑨ Carrie has 11 bags of 56 beans each. If she wants to put them equally in 8 bags, how many beans will there be in each bag?

_____

⑩ Jonathan jogs for 25 min every 5 days. At the same rate, how many minutes does he jog for in a common year?

_____

⑪ Erin stacked 12 towers of 24 blocks each. How many blocks will be in each tower if she restacks them into 9 towers with the same number of blocks in each?

_____

⑫ 738 light bulbs are put in packs of 6. If each pack of light bulbs is sold for $11, how much do the light bulbs cost altogether?

_____

⑬ Jodie works 4-hour shifts and earns $15 each hour. If she made $840, how many shifts did she work?

_____

⑭ An admission ticket to the zoo is $4. The total cost of the students' tickets was $960.

We went to the zoo on 6 school buses. How many students were there on each bus?

_____

Operations with Whole Numbers (2)

• adding, subtracting, multiplying, and dividing whole numbers

Try It

Elly eats 2 strawberries after each meal. If she has 3 meals a day, how many strawberries will she eat in 1 week?

She will eat _____ strawberries.

Read This

Read the questions carefully to determine what operation(s) to use. Solving a question can involve multiple operations.

Lawrence works in a lumber yard. Solve the problems. Show your work.

① There are 752 pine planks, 598 oak planks, and 208 maple planks. Each plank is 2 m long.

a. How many planks are there in all?

_____

b. The pine and maple planks are bundled together into groups of 8. How many bundles are there?

_____

c. If 112 bundles of pine and maple planks are sold, how many metres of lumber is sold in all?

_____

d. If 269 oak planks are sold, how many metres of oak is left?

_____

Solve the problems. Show your work.

② Fran's class has 12 boys and 11 girls. Each student was given 3 pencils. After the pencils were given out, there were 7 left.

a.
> How many pencils were given out in total?

_____

b. If the pencils came in packs of 4, how many packs of pencils were there at the start?

_____

③ A group of friends played a game in which they measured how far they could throw a ball.

Name	Distance (cm)
Mario	1236
Sandy	1805
Danny	1475
Jimmy	1938
Dolores	1647

a. How much farther did Jimmy throw than Sandy?

_____

b. If Mario and Jimmy were on a team against Sandy and Dolores, which team had a greater total distance?

_____

c. If Danny got to double his distance because he had no teammates, how much farther did the winning team throw than Danny?

_____

④ A mansion has 11 French doors and 32 windows. Each French door has 8 panes of glass and each window has 2. A cleaning company cleans the doors for $15 per 2 panes and the windows for $12 per pane.

a. How many panes of glass are there in all?

b. How much does it cost to clean the windows?

_____

_____

c. How much does it cost to clean the panes of glass in the doors?

d. The cleaning company is having a $250-off sale. How much does it cost to clean all the panes of glass?

_____

_____

⑤ Ms. Wiz bought 9 rolls of ribbon. They have a total length of 108 m. She takes one of the rolls and cuts it into 20-cm strips. How many strips are there?

Tips

1 m = 100 cm

_____

⑥ Peter mixed 510 mL of orange juice with 378 mL of pineapple juice to make fruit punch. If he pours it all equally in 4 cups, how much fruit punch will there be in each cup?

_____

⑦ A jacket cost $75 and a pair of jeans cost $34. If John bought 2 jackets and 3 pairs of jeans, how much did he pay?

_____

⑧ Mario wants two CDs. One of them is $15 and the other is $18. If Mario has a $20 bill, a $10 bill, and a $5 bill, can he afford the two CDs?

_____

⑨ It takes Sandy 20 minutes to walk to a library or 14 minutes to run there. How much time can she save in a week if she runs to and from the library each day instead of walking?

_____

⑩ Brian has a coin that doubles in value every 7 years. If it is worth $55 now, how much will it be worth in 21 years?

_____

⑪
I collect hockey cards. The first album has 382 cards. The second album has 148 more cards than the first.

If Sally wants to rearrange the hockey cards equally into 3 albums, how many cards will there be in each album?

_____

3 Decimals (1)

- solving word problems involving decimals

Try It

Jerry has 79.8 g of paprika and 80.68 g of cumin. How much do the spices weigh in all?

79.8 + 80.68 = ▢

They weigh _____ g in all.

placeholder

$$79.8\textbf{0}$$
$$+\ 80.68$$
$$\overline{}$$

Read This

Remember that zeros at the end of a decimal number can be dropped.

e.g.   2.90 ⟶ 2.9

8.00 ⟶ 8

Zeros can also be added as placeholders to help keep numbers aligned.

Solve the problems. Show your work.

① Franco pours 0.75 L of orange juice and 1.28 L of apple juice into a jug. How much juice is there in the jug?

_____

② Lisa takes out 2.68 kg of peanuts from a 5-kg bag of peanuts. How many kilograms of peanuts are left in the bag?

_____

③ Matthew paid $8.60 for 10 juice boxes. How much did each juice box cost?

_____

④ It costs $35.50 to rent a lawn mower for 1 day. How much does it cost to rent a lawn mower for 10 days?

_____

⑤ Kevin had $39.55. He spent $28.62 on toys. How much money does he have left?

_____

⑥ Janet measures the height of two trees. The first tree is 1.83 m tall and the second one is 0.27 m shorter. How tall is the second tree?

_____

⑦ A toy car weighs 215.62 g and a toy train weighs 360.82 g. How much do the toys weigh altogether?

_____

⑧ Johnny finished the race in 2.31 hours. How much faster was Kelly if she finished it in 1.92 hours?

_____

⑨ 1000 bars of soap weigh 120 kg. What is the weight of each bar of soap?

_____

⑩ A ketchup packet holds 9.46 mL of ketchup. How much ketchup do 100 packets hold altogether?

_____

⑪ Kirk spent $8.55 on lunch and Jenna spent $11.29.

    a. How much more did Jenna spend on lunch than Kirk?

_____

    b. How much did they spend on lunch altogether?

_____

⑫ Jordan has $50. He wants to buy a baseball cap for $19.99 and a basketball jersey for $25.45.

    a. How much do the two items cost altogether?

_____

    b. Does Jordan have enough to buy the items? If so, how much will he have left after buying them? If not, how much more does he need?

_____

⑬

Cape Trail is 5.9 km long and we've already walked 1.38 km!

    a. How much farther do David and his dad have to walk to complete the trail?

_____

    b. Black Bird Trail is 1.25 km longer than Cape Trail. How long is Black Bird Trail?

_____

⑭ Napkins are sold in small and large boxes. A small box costs $2.49 and a large box costs $20.58.

a. What is the cost of 10 small boxes of napkins?

_____

b. What is the price difference between a large box and 10 small boxes?

_____

⑮ 100 pencils cost $35 and an eraser costs $0.59. What is the total cost of 2 pencils and an eraser?

_____

⑯

I'm reading the nutrition facts on this jar of jelly beans.

Nutrition Facts
1 Serving (10 pieces)
Sugar...7.7 g
Salt......5.5 mg

a. How much sugar is there in 10 servings?

_____

b. How much salt is there in one jelly bean?

_____

c. How much sugar is there in 1000 jelly beans?

_____

4 Decimals (2)

- solving word problems involving decimals

Mark bought 10 trading cards for $0.57 each. He paid with a $10 bill. What was his change?

Cost of cards: $0.57 x 10 = ☐

Change: $10 – ☐ = ☐

His change was ☐ .

Read This

For addition and subtraction, add "0" as a placeholder when needed. For multiplication and division by 10, 100, and 1000, make sure you move the decimal point the correct number of places in the correct direction.

Read the sale flyer of A&K Store. Solve the problems. Show your work.

① What is the total cost of 1 T-shirt and 1 USB?

_____

② The original price of a USB was $16. How much did John save if he bought 10 USBs?

_____

A&K Store — SALE

$12.37

2 for $1.59

$14.62

$67.99

③ Jenny bought 2 pairs of shoes. What was her change from $150?

④ Cam bought a T-shirt, 2 pens, and a pair of shoes. What was the total price of these items?

_____   _____

See the costs of the items. Solve the problems. Show your work.

⑤

$9.50   2 for $18.20 $21.35   10 pairs for $14.85 $15.09

a. How much do a tie and a belt cost altogether?

_____

b. How much do 2 blouses and a dress cost in all?

_____

c. How much do 20 pairs of socks cost?

_____

d. How much do 100 pairs of socks cost?

_____

e.

I have a $20-off coupon. If I buy 10 ties, how much
do I need to pay?

_____

⑥ A 1000-seat theatre sells tickets for $8.50 each and bags of popcorn for $5.32 each.

a. How much will the theatre make if all the tickets are sold?

_____

b. How much will the theatre make if 100 bags of popcorn are sold?

_____

c. A gift certificate can be redeemed for a ticket and a bag of popcorn. How much do 10 gift certificates cost?

_____

d. A discount of $2.86 per gift certificate is given for purchases of 100 gift certificates or more. How much do 100 gift certificates cost?

_____

⑦ A sushi restaurant offers two promotions. Promotion A is a party tray of 100 pieces of sushi for $89.38. Promotion B is an all-you-can-eat deal for $24.99 per person.

a. How much does it cost altogether for three people to have all-you-can-eat sushi?

_____

b. A group of 4 people will eat about 100 pieces of sushi. If they order a party tray instead of getting the all-you-can-eat deal, how much will they save?

_____

Use the map to solve the problems. Show your work.

⑧

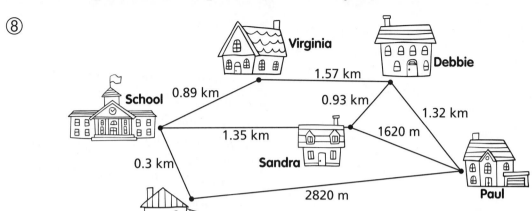

Virginia

Debbie

1.57 km

School 0.89 km

0.93 km

1.32 km

1.35 km

1620 m

0.3 km Sandra

2820 m

Paul

Rachel

* This map is not drawn to scale.

a. Who lives closest to the school?
   What is the distance in metres?

   _____

b. What is the distance in kilometres between Sandra's house and Paul's house?

Tips

1 km = 1000 m

m → km	km → m
• divide by 1000	• multiply by 1000
e.g.	e.g.
15 m	7.2 km
↓ ÷ 1000	↓ x 1000
0.015 km	7200 m

   _____

c. How far is it from Debbie's house to the school if she passes by Virginia's house?

   _____

d. Compare the routes. What is the shortest distance in metres from Debbie's house to the school?

   _____

5 Fractions

- solving word problems involving fractions

Try It

Sally biked $\frac{2}{3}$ of a trail and Kari biked $\frac{3}{4}$. Who biked farther?

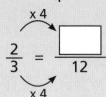

$$\frac{2}{3} = \frac{}{12}$$ (×4) $$\frac{3}{4} = \frac{}{12}$$ (×3)

 biked farther.

Read This

To compare fractions with different denominators, first find their common denominator. Write equivalent fractions with the common denominator as their denominators. The one with the greater numerator is the greater fraction.

Colour the diagrams to help solve the problems.

① Tim and Ann each had a chocolate bar. Tim ate $\frac{1}{3}$ of his and Ann ate $\frac{2}{5}$ of hers. Who ate less?

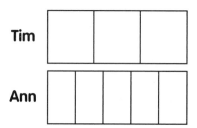

_____

② May served $\frac{3}{7}$ of a cake and then ate $\frac{2}{8}$. Did she serve or eat more cake?

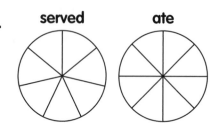

_____

③ Ken was building two toy trains. He built $\frac{7}{10}$ of the red train and $\frac{8}{12}$ of the blue train. Which train did he build more of?

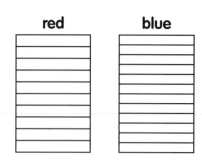

_____

④ Dan and Ian are playing a card game. Dan has $\frac{1}{4}$ of the cards and Ian has $\frac{4}{13}$. Who has more cards?

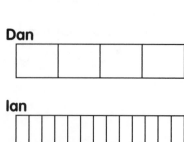

_____

Look at the pictures and answer the questions.

⑤ 4 children share the fruits in the bowl equally. What fraction of each type of fruit does each child get?

_____

⑥ On Halloween, Dan shares his chocolate bars with his friends. What fraction of the chocolate bars will each child get if they are shared equally among

   a. 6 children?

_____

   b. 4 children?

_____

Answer the questions.

⑦ Peter's hat size is $6\frac{1}{2}$. Joe's is $6\frac{3}{8}$. Whose hat size is larger?

_____

⑧ Nina ran $5\frac{3}{5}$ km. Jenna ran $5\frac{3}{4}$ km. Who ran farther?

_____

⑨ Bob's eatery used $3\frac{1}{6}$ boxes of napkins in a day, while Jim's eatery used $3\frac{3}{10}$. Whose eatery used fewer napkins?

_____

⑩ If Mary read a story in $\frac{1}{2}$ hour and Jill read it in 42 minutes, who read it faster?

_____

⑪ There are 30 students in Mrs. Ling's class.

a. $\frac{2}{5}$ of the students are girls. How many girls are there in the class?

_____

b. On Friday, $\frac{1}{6}$ of the students were away. How many students were not in class on Friday?

If you divide 30 students into 5 equal groups, each group will have 6 students.

So, $\frac{1}{5}$ of 30 is 6.

_____

c. 9 students have sandwiches for lunch. What fraction of the students have sandwiches for lunch?

_____

⑫ 5 of the 26 letters in the alphabet are vowels. The other letters are consonants. What fraction of the alphabet do consonants make up?

_____

⑬ Tom worked 18 out of 30 days in September. What fraction of the month did he work?

_____

⑭ Carly says that $\frac{15}{4}$ is greater than $\frac{13}{3}$ since 15 > 13 and 4 > 3. Is this statement true or false? Explain.

_____

Jon is having a party. Help him solve the problems.

⑮

There are 12 children at my party.

a. 3 pizzas are divided equally among them. How much pizza does each child get?

_____

b. $\frac{1}{3}$ of the children are girls. How many girls are there at the party?

_____

c. The birthday cake is divided into 16 equal slices. If each child eats 1 slice, what fraction of the cake is left over?

_____

⑯ The children play in the backyard for $\frac{1}{2}$ h, watch TV for $\frac{3}{5}$ h, and have snacks for $\frac{3}{4}$ h.

a. Which activity takes the most time?

_____

b. Which activity takes the least time?

_____

⑰ The children made spinners of the same size. Jon gave his spinner 12 equal sections and coloured 9. Ali gave her spinner 18 equal sections and coloured 14. Who coloured more of their spinner?

_____

6 Operations with Money

- solving word problems involving money

Try It

Mary pays $14.95 for a book with 2 $10 bills. How much change will she get back?

Amount paid: ☐

Change: ☐ – $14.95 = ☐

She will get ☐ back.

Read This

When solving money-related problems, look for key phrases and words to help determine what operation to use.

addition
- finding the "total"

subtraction
- finding money "saved"
- making "change"
- finding how much "more"

Ben started a summer business. Read the table about his services and the service fees. Solve the problems. Show your work.

① If Mrs. Dory hires Ben to rake her leaves and mow her lawn, what will her bill be?

_____

② Mr. Ryan hired Ben to do all the jobs except the car wash.

a. What was his bill?

_____

b. Mr. Ryan gave Ben a $100 bill. How much change did he get back?

_____

Ben's Cleaning Service

Service	Fee
Leaf Raking	$15.48
Driveway Sweeping	$10.09
Lawn Mowing	$35.17
Garage Cleaning	$48.74
Car Washing	$9.76

$12.50 off on orders of 3 services or more

③ Mrs. Winter hired Ben to do 2 jobs. If her bill was $25.24, which 2 jobs did Ben do?

_____

Emily runs a candy store. The money that she earned over 4 weeks is shown.
Solve the problems. Show your work.

④ How much did Emily earn in each week?

_____

_____

_____

⑤ How much was earned in the first two weeks?

_____

⑥ How much more money was earned in Week 4 than Week 3?

_____

⑦ How much was earned over the four weeks altogether?

_____

⑧ If the cost of the candies sold was $528.25, how much profit did Emily make?

_____

Week 1

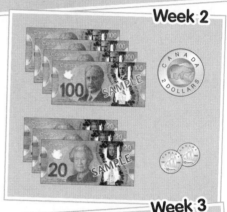
Week 2

Week 3

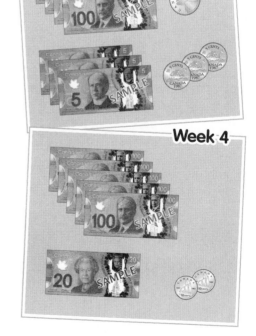
Week 4

LEVEL 3 – APPLICATIONS

John and Stacy are shopping for hiking supplies. Find how much money each child has. Then solve the problems.

$25.45 $30.80 $42.35 $52.15 $19.99

⑨

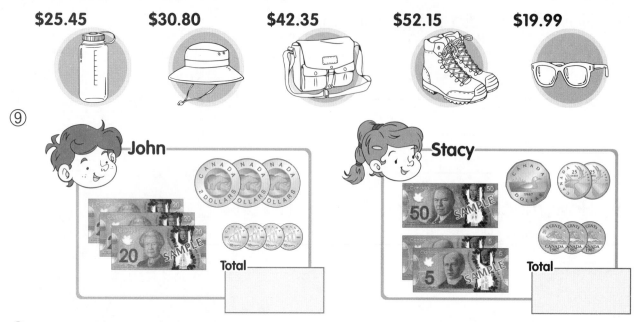

John

Total

Stacy

Total

⑩ How much do the bag and the boots cost together?

_____

⑪ How much will Stacy have left if she buys the hat and the sunglasses?

_____

⑫ How much will John have left if he buys 2 water bottles?

_____

⑬ Do John and Stacy have enough money altogether to buy 1 of each item?

_____

Solve the problems. Show your work.

⑭ Donna and her friends went to a new candy store to buy their favourite candies.

   a. Lollipops cost $1.19 each or $10.80 for a package of 10. If Donna wanted 10 lollipops, how much would she save by buying a package of 10?

   _____

   b. Donna bought 2 packages of lollipops with $25. What was her change?

   _____

⑮ Edward's Emporium is having a year-end sale. Customers get $1.50 off every $10. For purchases over $100, customers get an additional $0.30 off every $10.

   a. Ann buys a blouse at $82.97. What is her change from a $100 bill?

   _____

   b. Tim buys a jacket at $120.45. What is the actual cost after the promotions?

   _____

   c. Ray buys 3 shirts at $16.99 each. How much money does he save? What is his change from a $50 bill?

   _____

   d. A pair of boots costs $92.85. If Sally wants to buy 2 pairs of boots, should she buy them separately or together? Explain.

   _____

7 Time

- solving word problems involving elapsed times

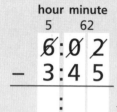

Try It

A movie starts at 3:45 p.m. and ends at 6:02 p.m. How long is the movie?

hour	minute
5	62

$$\begin{array}{r} \cancel{6}:\cancel{0}\,2 \\ -\ 3:4\,5 \\ \hline : \end{array}$$

⟵ elapsed time

1. Align the hours and minutes.
2. Subtract the minutes. Regroup if needed.
3. Subtract the hours.

Read This

Use subtraction to find the elapsed time. Subtract the minutes first and then the hours. Regroup 1 hour as 60 minutes if needed.

The movie is _____ h _____ min long.

The table shows the start and end times of different movies. Find the duration of each movie. Show your work.

①

Movie	Start Time	End Time	Duration
Tea, Please!	1:30 p.m.	3:46 p.m.	_____ h _____ min
Endless Planet	8:15 p.m.	10:07 p.m.	
The Doll Boss	10:36 a.m.	12:30 p.m.	
Silent Screech	5:28 p.m.	8:00 p.m.	
Fire Prince	3:47 p.m.	6:08 p.m.	
Love Together	7:55 p.m.	9:29 p.m.	

Tea, Please!

$$\begin{array}{r} 3:46 \\ -\ 1:30 \\ \hline \Box:\Box \end{array}$$

Endless Planet

Hint: 1 h = 60 min

The Doll Boss

Silent Screech

Fire Prince

Love Together

Read what Jimmy says. Solve the problems. Show your work.

②

Grandpa and I left home at 9:40 a.m. this morning for a walk to the park. It took us 57 min to get there. After spending 40 min at the park, we walked to a grocery store, which took 32 min. We shopped for 17 min and then walked home, arriving at 12:42 p.m.

Jimmy

a. What time did Jimmy and his grandpa

• reach the park?

_____

• leave the park?

_____

• reach the grocery store?

_____

• leave the grocery store?

_____

b. How long did it take them to walk home from the grocery store?

_____

c. How long did they walk in total?

_____

d. How much longer did they spend at the park than the grocery store?

_____

e. How long were they away from home?

_____

Daniel has audio recordings of birds singing in his backyard. Find how long each recording is in two ways.

③ 🐦🎤 **11:30 a.m. to 1:40 p.m.**

Breaking into 2 Parts	24-hour Notation
• from 11:30 a.m. to noon: _____	11:30 a.m. → _____ 1:40 p.m. → _____
• from noon to 1:40 p.m.: _____	⬚ : ⬚ − ⬚ : ⬚ ⬚ : ⬚
• Total: _____	

This recording is _____ long.

Hints

To find the elapsed time when the time starts before noon and ends after noon, you can use two ways:

• break the time into 2 parts
• convert the time into 24-hour notation

e.g. from 11:15 a.m. to 2:08 p.m.

Breaking into 2 Parts	24-hour Notation
• from 11:15 a.m. to noon: 45 min	11:15 a.m. → 11:15 2:08 p.m. → 14:08
• from noon to 2:08 p.m.: 2 h 8 min	14:08 − 11:15 2:53
45 min + 2 h 8 min = 2 h 53 min	

So, the elapsed time is 2 h 53 min.

④ 🐦🎤 **10:58 a.m. to 1:07 p.m.**

It is _____ long.

⑤ 🐦🎤 **9:12 a.m. to 2:02 p.m.**

It is _____ long.

⑥ 🐦🎤 **11:21 p.m. to 2:13 a.m.**

It is _____ long.

⑦ 🐦🎤 **10:35 a.m. to 5:43 p.m.**

It is _____ long.

Solve the problems. Show your work.

⑧ Larry worked on his science project on Sunday.

a. He started the project at 8:16 a.m. and stopped at 4:05 p.m. How long did he work on it?

b. He spent 2 h 20 min doing research at the library. He left at 3:32 p.m. What time did he start his work at the library?

_____

_____

⑨ Gary went to a movie theatre.

a. To get there, he left home at 10:26 a.m., took a bus for 37 min, and then walked for 16 min. What time did he reach the theatre?

b. Movie A lasts 1 h 43 min; Movie B lasts 1 h 16 min. If Movie A starts at 11:45 a.m. and Movie B starts at 12:10 p.m., which movie finishes first?

_____

_____

⑩ a.

It takes me 23 min to walk to the doctor's office. If I leave home at 1:48 p.m., will I be on time for my 2:15 p.m. appointment?

b.

My favourite TV show starts at 11:45 a.m. and lasts for 1 h 35 min. What time does the show end?

_____

_____

8 Perimeter and Area

- solving word problems involving perimeters and areas

What is the perimeter of the garden? What is the area?

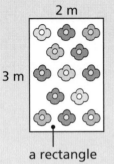

2 m

3 m

a rectangle

Perimeter: 2 x _____ + 2 x _____

= _____ (m)

Area: _____ x _____

= _____ (m²)

The perimeter is [ ] and

the area is [ ].

Remember these formulas for finding the perimeters and areas of squares and rectangles.

s

square

Perimeter: 4 x s

Area: s x s

l

w rectangle

Perimeter: 2 x l + 2 x w

Area: l x w

Answer the questions. Show your work.

① Cam is shown 4 different tiles for his kitchen.

a. Find the perimeter and area of each tile.

A   5 cm   3 cm

A

B

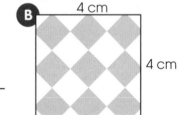

B   4 cm   4 cm

_____

C

D

C   2 cm   6 cm

b. If 16 Tile Bs were arranged in a 4-by-4 square, what would the perimeter be?

_____

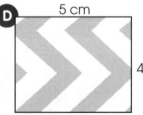

D   5 cm   4 cm

c. What is the area of 100 Tile Ds?

_____

_____

② The dimensions of a picture are 20 cm by 12 cm. The picture is put in a frame that is 3 cm wide on each side.

a. What are the dimensions of the framed picture?

_____

b. What is the perimeter of the framed picture?

_____

c. What is the area of the framed picture?

_____

③ Jeff's old computer monitor measures 30 cm by 20 cm. His new monitor measures 60 cm by 40 cm, which doubles the old one.

a. Does the perimeter of the new monitor also double that of the old monitor? If not, describe their relationship.

_____

b. Does the area of the new monitor also double that of the old monitor? If not, describe their relationship.

_____

④ Measure the length and width of this book to the nearest centimetre. What are the perimeter and area of the book?

_____

Look at the floor plan and dimensions of Darren's apartment unit. Answer the questions.

⑤

Floor Plan

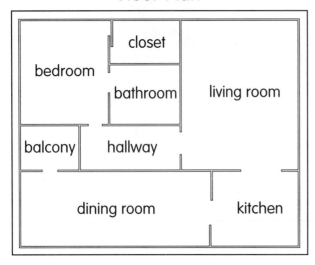

Room	Dimensions
bedroom	7 m x 6 m
closet	3 m x 5 m
bathroom	4 m x 5 m
balcony	3 m x 4 m
hallway	3 m x 7 m
living room	10 m x 8 m
dining room	5 m x 13 m
kitchen	5 m x 6 m

a. What is the perimeter of
  • the bathroom?

  _____

  • the living room?

  _____

  • the dining room and kitchen combined?

  _____

  • the hallway and living room combined?

  _____

b. What is the area of
  • the closet?

  _____

  • the balcony?

  _____

  • the living room and the kitchen?

  _____

  • the bedroom and the closet?

  _____

c. What are the perimeter and area of Darren's unit?

_____

Solve the problems. Show your work.

⑥ A table is 5 m long and 2 m wide. What are its perimeter and area?

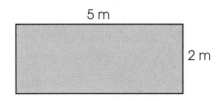

_____

⑦ The length of a square coffee table is 60 cm. What are its perimeter and area?

_____

⑧ A square has a perimeter of 120 cm. How long is each side?

_____

⑨ A rectangular backyard has an area of 400 m². If its length is 25 m, what is its width?

_____

⑩ A piece of rectangular cardboard has a perimeter of 46 cm. If its width is 5 cm, what is its area?

_____

⑪ There are 2 L-shaped bedrooms in a house.

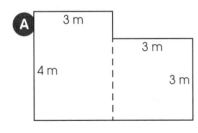

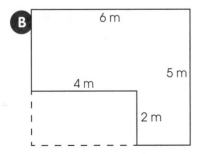

a. If baseboard is installed along the bottom of the walls, how much baseboard is needed for both rooms?

_____

b. Laminate flooring is installed in both rooms. Which room needs more laminate to cover its floor?

_____

LEVEL 3 – APPLICATIONS

9 Volume, Capacity, and Mass

- solving word problems involving the volume, capacity, and mass

Try It

Gary has an aquarium with the measurements shown. What are its volume and capacity?

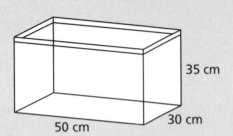

35 cm

50 cm

30 cm

Read This

Make sure that you use the correct units of measure to answer word problems.

Volume: cm³, m³

Capacity: mL, L

Mass: mg, g, kg, t

Volume: _____ x _____ x _____ = _____ (cm³)

$\div 1000$

Capacity: _____ cm³ = _____ mL = _____ L

The volume is ☐ and the capacity is ☐ .

Sketch the objects and label their measurements. Then solve the problems. Show your work.

① Sandy has two aquariums. The old one is 45 cm long, 15 cm wide, and 20 cm tall. The new one is 60 cm long, 25 cm wide, and 40 cm tall.

　　a. Sketch the aquariums.

　　b. What are the capacities of the aquariums in litres?

old aquarium

_____

new aquarium

c. If the old aquarium is full and the new one is half full, which aquarium has more water? By how much?

_____

Read what Alan says. Then answer the questions. Show your work.

②
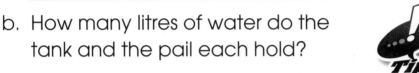
A tank is full with 160 000 mL of water. I'm trying to empty it with this rectangular pail.

a. What is the volume of the pail?

20 cm
10 cm
25 cm

_____

b. How many litres of water do the tank and the pail each hold?

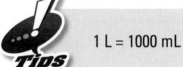
1 L = 1000 mL

Tips

_____

c. If Alan removes 8 pails of water,

• what volume of the tank will be empty?

_____

• how many litres of water will remain in the tank?

_____

d. How many pails of water must be removed for the tank to be half empty?

_____

e. If Alan is emptying the water into an aquarium that is 1 m long and 0.25 m wide, what is the minimum height of the aquarium needed to hold all the water from the tank?

_____

f. If Alan puts 6 metal balls of the same volume into the tank and 75 000 cm³ of water overflows, what is the volume of each metal ball?

_____

LEVEL 3 – APPLICATIONS

Read what each child says. Determine and write whether each of them is asking about the volume (V), capacity (C), or mass (M). Then write the most appropriate unit for measuring it.

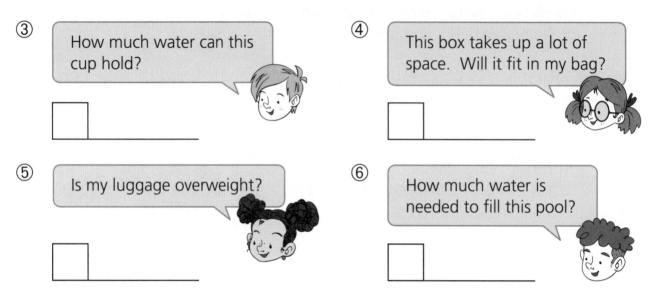

③ How much water can this cup hold?

④ This box takes up a lot of space. Will it fit in my bag?

⑤ Is my luggage overweight?

⑥ How much water is needed to fill this pool?

Solve the problems. Show your work.

⑦ Baby Jack weighed 3.2 kg at birth and gained 100 g per week. How much did he weigh after 5 weeks?

_____

⑧ An elevator holds a maximum weight of 1.4 t. If the average mass of an adult is 70 kg, how many adults can the elevator hold at most?

_____

⑨ A vanilla birthday cake is 12 cm by 12 cm by 4 cm. It is cut into 16 equal pieces.

   a. What is the volume of each piece?

   b. If the whole cake is 1 kg 360 g, what is the mass of each piece?

_____   _____

⑩ A nickel weighs about 5 g. How many nickels weigh 1 kg altogether?

_____

⑪ A lumber yard sells 100 kg of logs for $50.
a. How much can the yard make from selling 30 t of logs?

_____

b. How much can the yard make from selling 30 000 g of logs?

_____

⑫ Sam can choose one of three gift boxes.
Which box has the greatest volume?

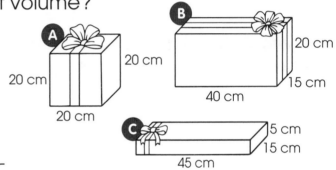

_____

⑬ Paul is decorating his fish tank. He drops 8 rocks into the tank and the water level rises by 2 cm.

a. What is the total volume of the 8 rocks?

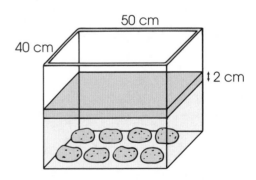

_____

b. What is the average volume of the rocks?

_____

10 Coordinate Systems

• solving word problems involving coordinate systems

Try It

Kari is at B2. If she moves 3 blocks east and 2 blocks north, where will she be?

"3 blocks east" = "3 blocks to the right"
"2 blocks north" = "2 blocks up"

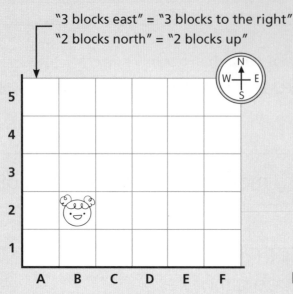

Read This

Coordinates are a set of letters and numbers that show you the position of something on a map. Remember to write the letter before the number.

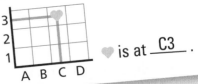

♥ is at __C3__ .

Kari will be at _____ .

Jack and Emily are playing a treasure hunt video game. Help them find the shortest routes to get the keys and the treasure. Then answer the question.

①

a. How should Jack move to get his key and then the treasure?

🔑 :

🧰 :

b. How should Emily move to get her key and then the treasure?

🔑 :

🧰 :

c. Who has the shorter route to the treasure?

_____

Lizzie recorded the location of her plants on the grid. Find the answers.

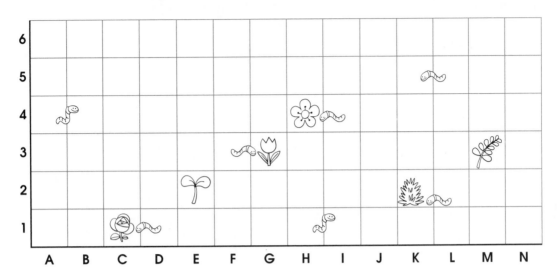

② Write the coordinates.

a. 🌱 _____

b. 🌸 _____

c. 🌿 _____

d. 🌹 _____

e. 🌷 _____

f. 🌾 _____

③ Lizzie decided to move two plants. Cross out the plants on the grid and draw to show where they are now.

I moved 🌱 1 unit west.
I moved 🌸 2 units east and 1 unit north.

④ Worms are crawling among the plants. Describe their movements from plant to plant.

a. 🌱 to 🌸 : _____

b. 🌿 to 🌹 : _____

c. 🌾 to 🌷 : _____

d. 🌸 to 🌹 : _____

e. 🌷 to 🌿 : _____

Josh and Kim each followed a trail to meet at the pond in Conservation Garden. Their paths are shown on the grid. Answer the questions.

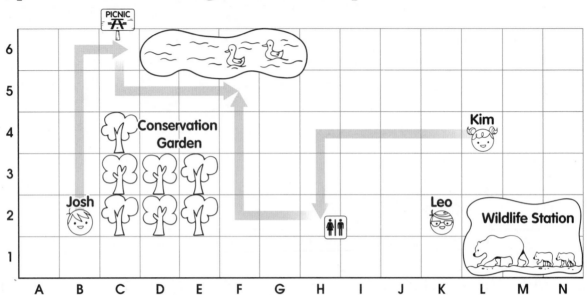

⑤ Colour the square that represents the meeting place. What are its coordinates?

_____

⑥ Describe the paths Josh and Kim took.

a. Josh was at _____ . He moved _____ block(s) _____ and _____ block(s) _____ . Then he moved _____

_____ .

b. Kim was at _____ . She moved _____

_____

_____ .

⑦ Leo is joining Josh and Kim. Describe the shortest path for Leo to take to the meeting place without crossing Josh's and Kim's paths.

_____

_____

Look at the torn pieces of the maps. Answer the questions.

⑧ Eva accidentally tore a map. She has two remaining pieces.

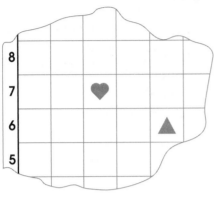 

a. Find the coordinates.

♥ _____   ▲ _____

✚ _____   ★ _____

b. Write how to move from

- ♥ to ★:

  _____

  _____

- ✚ to ▲:

  _____

  _____

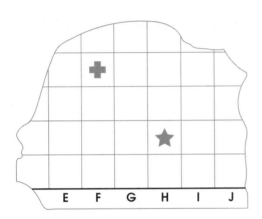

⑨ John's map was torn and the letters and numbers are now missing. However, John remembers that 🚒 is at H6.

a. Find the coordinates.

b. John is 5 squares south of 🛋. What are his coordinates and how should he move to reach 🗑 ?

_____

_____

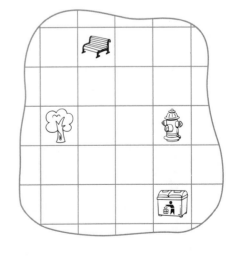

Transformations

- solving problems involving transformations

Try It

Below are pictures of a road sign taken before and after a windstorm. Describe the transformation.

before **after**

There are three types of transformations – translation, reflection, and rotation. They do not change the original size of a shape.

_____

Look at the shapes drawn on the grid. Do the transformations and draw the images.

 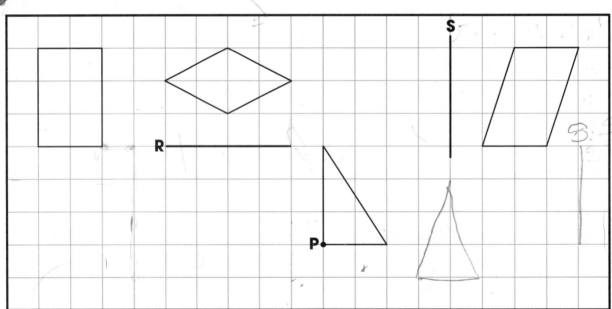

a. Translate the rectangle 1 unit to the right and 4 units down.

b. Reflect the rhombus in Line R.

 c. Rotate the triangle $\frac{1}{4}$ clockwise about Point P.

d. Reflect the parallelogram in Line S. Then translate the image 5 units to the right and 4 units down.

The children are doing transformations with the letters of their names. Draw the images.

② Help Tia rotate her name.

T: $\frac{1}{4}$ turn counterclockwise

I: $\frac{1}{4}$ turn clockwise

A: $\frac{1}{2}$ turn

③ Help Ivy translate her name.

I: 4 units to the right and 3 units down

V: 2 units to the right and 2 units up

Y: 3 units to the left and 4 units up

● = centres of rotation

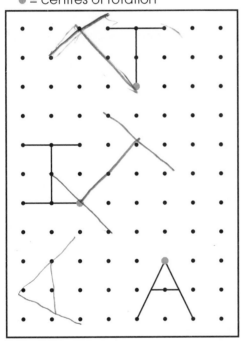

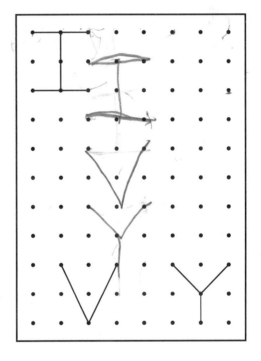

④ Help Hannah Atwood reflect her initials in the lines of reflection.

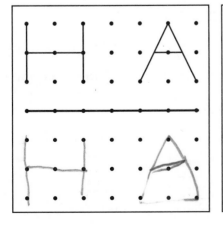

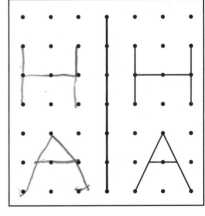

Sam turns a picture to see different ways to hang it. Answer the questions.

⑤ I'm making a $\frac{1}{4}$ turn counterclockwise repeatedly with the picture.

Check the set of diagrams that shows Sam's rotations.

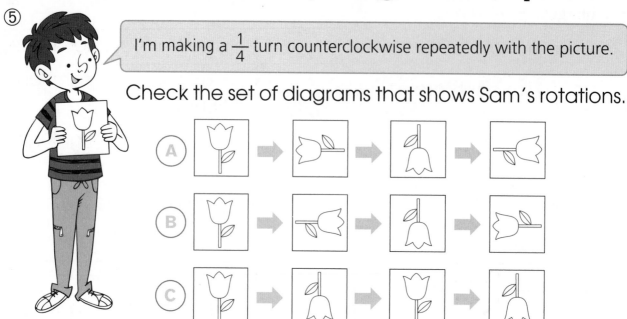

⑥ Draw to show the movement of the picture if Sam

a. makes a $\frac{1}{4}$ turn clockwise repeatedly.

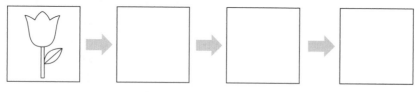

b. makes a $\frac{1}{2}$ turn repeatedly.

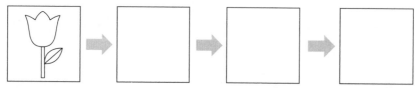

⑦ Circle the shape and letter Sam is talking about.

a. Sam says, "No matter how I turn this shape, it always looks the same."

b. Sam says, "This letter looks the same after every $\frac{1}{2}$ turn."

Sketch to help the children see what the pictures will look like. Then answer the question.

⑧ What will this picture look like when it is turned $\frac{1}{4}$ clockwise?

⑨ What will this picture look like if I do a handstand and look at it?

⑩ I put this picture on a grid. If I move it 2 units up and 3 units down, how will it look?

⑪ If I look at this picture in the mirror, what will it look like?

⑫ If 🧒 holds 🅰 instead of Ⓚ, will the image in the mirror be different from the picture she holds? Explain.

_____

_____

12 Patterning

- solving problems involving patterns

Try It

Mary does push-ups every day and records her results.

Day	1	2	3	4
No. of Push-ups	2	4	6	8

Read This

Find the pattern rule to relate the first set of numbers to the second set. Then solve the problem by using the pattern rule.

If the pattern continues, how many push-ups will I do on Day 6?

She will do [ ] push-ups on Day 6.

Follow the patterns to complete the tables. Then answer the questions.

① Billy was practising his basketball shot. He kept track of the number of baskets he made each day.

Day	1	2	3	4	5
No. of Baskets	1	3	5		

If the pattern continues,

a. how many baskets will Billy make on Day 6?

_____

b. on which day will Billy make 15 baskets?

_____

② Rob bought a used car. Its value drops every year.

Year	1	2	3	4	5
Value ($)	8000	4000	2000		

If the pattern continues,

a. in which year will the car be worth $\frac{1}{8}$ of its Year 1 value?

_____

b. what will its value be in Year 7?

_____

Help Tony complete the table. Then answer the questions.

③

I have 12 yellow marbles and 5 blue marbles. Each day I buy 2 yellow marbles and 3 blue marbles.

Day	1	2	3	4	5	6
No. of Yellow Marbles	12					
No. of Blue Marbles	5					

a. How many yellow marbles does Tony have on Day 7?

_____

b. How many blue marbles does Tony have on Day 8?

_____

c. On which day will Tony have 28 yellow marbles?

_____

d. On which day will Tony have 29 blue marbles?

_____

e. On which day will Tony have the same number of yellow and blue marbles?

_____

f. How many marbles does Tony have in all on Day 6?

_____

Joshua started a dog care business. Look at the rates for the services Joshua offers. Complete the tables with charges based on those rates. Then answer the questions.

④

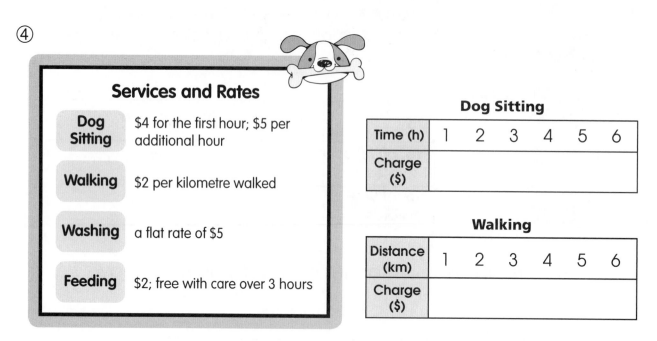

Services and Rates

Dog Sitting — $4 for the first hour; $5 per additional hour

Walking — $2 per kilometre walked

Washing — a flat rate of $5

Feeding — $2; free with care over 3 hours

Dog Sitting

Time (h)	1	2	3	4	5	6
Charge ($)						

Walking

Distance (km)	1	2	3	4	5	6
Charge ($)						

a. Tina purchased 10 hours of dog sitting. What was the charge?

_____

b. Kevin paid for 4 hours of dog sitting and a 3-km walk. What was the total charge?

_____

c. Lily wanted her poodle walked for 4 km and then washed. How much was her bill?

_____

d. Dolly asked Joshua for 8 hours of dog sitting. She wanted the dog washed and fed as well. How much was her bill?

_____

Mrs. Faam made a table with numbers for her class. Help the class complete the table. Then answer the questions.

⑤

This table contains 6 columns and 5 rows. The numbers in each column and row follow a pattern.

	Column 1	Column 2	Column 3	Column 4	Column 5	Column 6
Row 1	2	4		8		12
Row 2					20	
Row 3			18			36
Row 4	8			32	40	
Row 5	10	20	30			60

a. What is the pattern rule of Column 3? What are the next 3 numbers after 30?

_____

b. What is the pattern rule of Row 2? What are the next 3 numbers after 24?

_____

c. Which of the columns follows the same pattern rule as Row 5? What is the pattern rule?

_____

d. Joe has 6 cards. The number of cards that he collects increases by 6 each day. Which row shows the pattern of Joe's cards? How many cards will he have after 5 days?

_____

e. Raymond spends $8 each day. Which row shows the total amount of money he has spent over 6 days? How much money will he have spent after 4 days?

_____

13 Data Analysis

• analyzing data in sets and graphs

Try It

Check the type of data each set is.

• Height of a tree: 1.8 m, 2.4 m, 3.1 m
  - (A) discrete data
  - (B) continuous data

• Size of families: 5, 1, 3, 4, 8
  - (A) discrete data
  - (B) continuous data

Read This

Discrete data can only include certain values, usually whole numbers. Continuous data can include any value in a range, even decimal values. Discrete data is usually counted while continuous data is usually measured.

e.g.
• Number of students in a class ← discrete data
• Weight of a dog over 10 months ← continuous data

Determine whether each set of data is discrete or continuous. Write the letters.

①

 A the number of different animals in a zoo

 B the temperature at each hour in a day

 C the total distance a runner ran each minute

 D the number of sandwiches sold each day in a week

 E the number of marbles in different colours in a jar

 F the height of a child over 12 months

 G the number of loonies saved over 10 weeks

Discrete Data _____   **Continuous Data** _____

Read what each child says. Determine which type of data he or she is describing and which type of graph suits it best.

②

I recorded the number of rainy days in each month of last year.

_____ data

_____ graph

Bar Graph
- to display categories
- to compare data

Line Graph
- to show the trend that a set of data follows over time

Circle Graph
- to show data that is part of a whole

③

I counted the number of candies in this jar by colour.

_____

_____

④

The roof is leaking water and I use a bucket to collect it. I measured the amount of water leaked each day.

_____   _____

⑤

I found out the fraction of people in each age group (i.e. infants, children, adults, seniors) in a city.

_____   _____

⑥

I looked up the number of tickets to new movies sold this summer.

_____   _____

Identify the graphs. Read each question. If the answer can be found, write the answer; otherwise, put a cross.

⑦

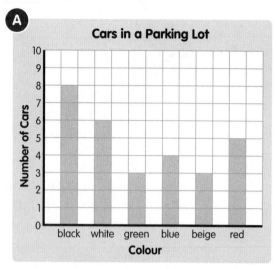

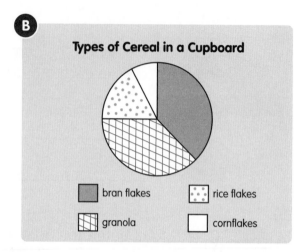

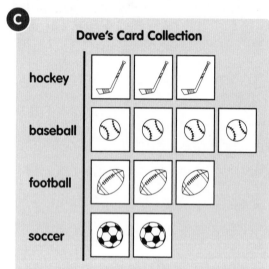

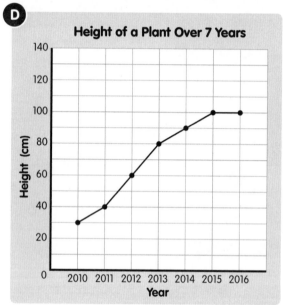

a. Type of Graph:

Ⓐ _____

Ⓑ _____

Ⓒ _____

Ⓓ _____

b. What is the mean number of sports cards? _____

c. What is the median number of cereal boxes? _____

d. What is the mode number of cars? _____

e. During which period did the plant's height remain unchanged? _____

Analyze each set of data. Check the correct answers and find the answers.

⑧ I did a survey and found the ages of 15 moviegoers at the theatre.

Ages of 15 Moviegoers	15	19	18	16	14	16	14	13
		11	13	14	15	16	17	14

a. Type of data:

Ⓐ discrete data

Ⓑ continuous data

b. Measures of central tendency:

_____ _____ _____
mean   median   mode

c. Most suitable graph to compare the number of moviegoers of each age:

Ⓐ bar graph   Ⓑ line graph   Ⓒ circle graph

---

⑨ **Numbers of Toonies Saved Over 6 Weeks**

Week	No. of Toonies Saved
1	10
2	15
3	1
4	6
5	10
6	12

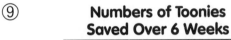

a. Type of data:

_____

b. Measures of central tendency:

_____ _____ _____
mean   median   mode

c. Most suitable graph to show the number of toonies saved over 6 weeks:

_____

---

⑩ **Amounts of Rainfall in 14 Days**

Day	Rainfall (mm)	Day	Rainfall (mm)
1	4.5	8	9.6
2	0	9	1.3
3	3.8	10	0
4	11	11	4.7
5	2.7	12	6.9
6	0	13	2.7
7	0	14	1.8

a. Type of data:

_____

b. Measures of central tendency:

_____ _____ _____
mean   median   mode

c. Most suitable graph to show the amounts of rainfall over 14 days:

_____

14 Graphs (1)

- reading graphs and answering questions about them

Try It

Which set of data is best represented by a line graph?
Check the circle.

(A) the weight of a baby over 12 months

(B) the number of sunny days in each month in a year

(C) the amount of work done by each student on a project

Read This

Line graphs are useful for showing how data changes over time.

Read the line graphs about Larry's toy car factory. Then answer the questions. Show your work.

① Larry recorded the number of toy cars produced at the factory last year.

a. How many toy cars were produced in January?

_____

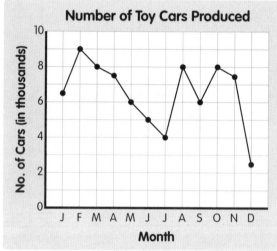

b. How many toy cars were produced from January to March?

_____

c. How many more toy cars were produced in June than July?

_____

d. The factory shut down for 2 weeks during the winter. In which month did it shut down?

_____

e. On average, how many toy cars were produced each month?

_____

② Larry kept track of the sales of two types of toy cars last year. The sales figures are displayed in the double line graph.

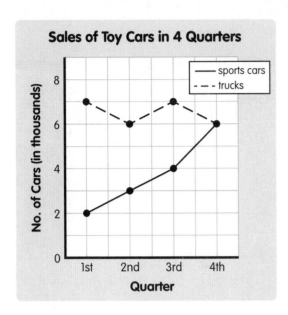

We sell many types of toy cars; sports cars and trucks are just two of them.

a. How many of each type of toy car were sold in the 3rd quarter?

_____

b. How many more sports cars were sold in the 4th quarter than the 1st quarter?

_____

c. How many trucks were sold from the 1st quarter to the 3rd quarter?

_____

d. In which quarter did Larry sell the same number of sports cars and trucks?

_____

e. What is the mean number of sports cars sold?

_____

Read the double bar graph. Then answer the questions.

③

Our community centre offers after-school activities for elementary school students. The double bar graph shows which grades our participants are in.

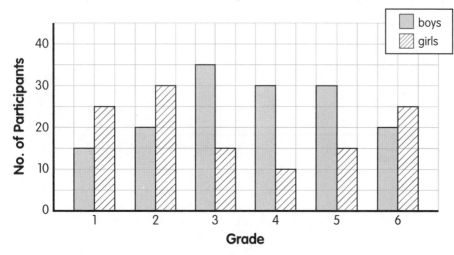

Number of Participants in Each Grade

a. What is the difference in the number of boys and girls in

• Grade 1?

_____

• Grade 4?

_____

b. In which grades are there more

• boys than girls participating?

_____

• girls than boys participating?

_____

c. What are the mean, median, and mode numbers of

• boys who participated in the activities?

_____

• girls who participated in the activities?

_____

Read the scenario and check the correct circle graph. Then answer the questions.

④ Erin's family loves fruits. She kept track of the amounts of money they spent on fruits in one week in the table.

Fruit	pears	bananas	apples	grapes
Money Spent	$5	$10	$15	$20

a. Check the circle graph that represents the data.

> We spent a total of $50.

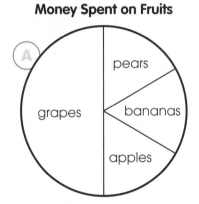

Money Spent on Fruits

Money Spent on Fruits

b. Which fruit did the family spend the most on? How much did they spend? Colour this section of the graph red.

_____

c. Which fruit did the family spend the least on? How much did they spend? Colour this section of the graph green.

_____

d. Which fruit takes up $\frac{1}{10}$ of the total amount spent?

_____

e. What fraction of the total amount was spent on apples?

_____

15 Graphs (2)

• making graphs and answering questions about them

Try It

Candice made a double bar graph representing the number of cakes and muffins in different flavours sold in her store last week.

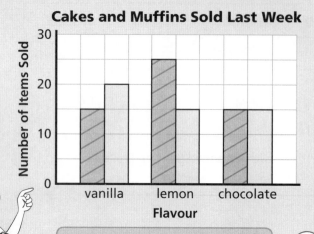

Cakes and Muffins Sold Last Week

Number of Items Sold (vertical axis: 0, 10, 20, 30)

Flavour (horizontal axis: vanilla, lemon, chocolate)

> More vanilla muffins were sold than vanilla cakes.

Read This

Be sure to add a legend to help your readers understand what data is displayed in a double bar graph or a double line graph.

Which is the correct legend?

A
▨ cakes
☐ muffins

B
▨ muffins
☐ cakes

Refer to the double bar graph above. Then answer the questions.

① Candice made the double bar graph using the data from a tally chart. Check the correct tally chart.

A

	cake	muffin
vanilla	⦀⦀ ⦀⦀ ⦀⦀	⦀⦀ ⦀⦀ ⦀⦀ |
lemon	⦀⦀ ⦀⦀ ⦀⦀ ⦀⦀	⦀⦀ ⦀⦀
chocolate	⦀⦀ ||	⦀⦀ ||

B

	cake	muffin
vanilla	⦀⦀ ⦀⦀ ⦀⦀	⦀⦀ ⦀⦀ ⦀⦀ ⦀⦀
lemon	⦀⦀ ⦀⦀ ⦀⦀ ⦀⦀ ⦀⦀	⦀⦀ ⦀⦀ ⦀⦀
chocolate	⦀⦀ ⦀⦀ ⦀⦀	⦀⦀ ⦀⦀ ⦀⦀

② Which lemon-flavoured item was more popular? How many more items were sold?

_____

③ In which flavour was there the same number of cakes and muffins sold?

_____

④ Were more cakes or muffins sold last week?

_____

The factory has two machines for packaging nuts. Complete the double bar graph to show the data in the tally chart. Then answer the questions.

⑤

	cashew	almond	peanut	walnut
Machine A (in thousands)	卌 卌 卌	卌 卌	卌 卌 卌 卌	卌 卌 卌
Machine B (in thousands)	卌 卌 卌 卌 卌	卌 卌 卌 卌	卌 卌 卌 卌	卌 卌

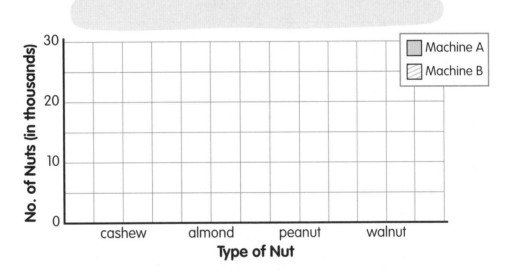

a. Which machine packaged more almonds? By how many?

_____

b. Which type of nut had the same quantity packaged by both machines? How many were packaged in total?

_____

c. Which type of nut did Machine A package the most of?

_____

d. The employees think that Machine B is more efficient. Do you agree? Explain.

_____

Darcy's and Horace's savings over the last 12 months are recorded in the table. Complete the double line graph and answer the questions.

⑥

Month	Child's Savings	
	Darcy	Horace
Jan	$6.50	$9.50
Feb	$7.25	$8.25
Mar	$4.50	$7.50
Apr	$9.50	$7
May	$9	$6.75
Jun	$6.50	$5.50
Jul	$5.25	$4.50
Aug	$6	$5.50
Sep	$7	$6
Oct	$7.50	$7.50
Nov	$8.75	$8
Dec	$9.25	$5

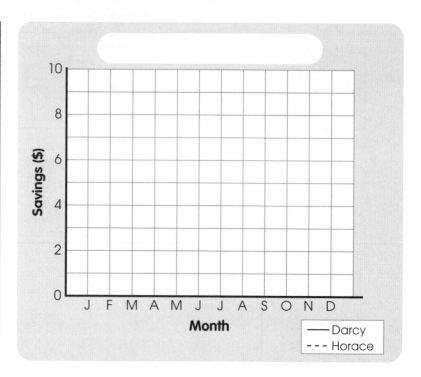

a. How much more savings did Horace have than Darcy in March?

_____

b. How much more savings did Horace have than Darcy in February?

_____

c. In which months did Horace have more savings than Darcy?

_____

d. How many months were Darcy's savings more than Horace's?

_____

e. In which month were their savings the same?

_____

f. What was Darcy's mean savings for the year?

_____

g. What was Horace's mean savings for the year?

_____

h. Who had more savings in total?

_____

50 scouts sold apples to raise money for charity. The number of apples each scout sold was recorded. Make a stem-and-leaf plot to organize the data. Then complete the circle graph and answer the questions.

⑦ **Apples Sold by 50 Scouts**

12	20	27	31	19	32	35	25	34	25	27	31	50
	15	40	39	54	35	40	42	25	32	40	38	42
24	31	15	19	21	29	34	29	28	29	34	27	21
	54	42	47	23	34	48	52	39	43	39	47	53

Stem	Leaf
1	
2	
3	
4	
5	

Apples Sold by 50 Scouts

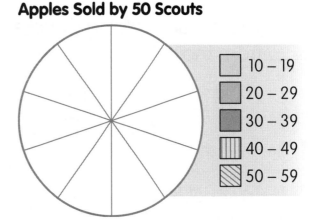

- 10 – 19
- 20 – 29
- 30 – 39
- 40 – 49
- 50 – 59

a. Which range accounts for $\frac{1}{5}$ of the number of apples sold?

_____

b. Which range takes up the same amount of space in the circle graph as the 20 – 29 range?

_____

c. Which two ranges take up more than half of the circle graph?

_____

d. I sold 19 apples. My friend, Emma, sold more apples and her range is twice the size of mine on the graph. Which range is Emma in?

_____

Probability

- solving word problems involving probability

Try It

Monique has a bag with 5 red balls and 7 green balls. If she picks a ball, what is the probability that the ball will be red?

The total number of outcomes: 5 + 7 = 12
The number of red balls: 5

The probability that the ball will be red is ☐ .

 Read This

When solving a probability problem, always start by determining the total number of outcomes.

Answer the questions.

① The children pick a marble from their bags.

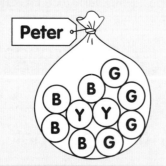

Emily

(B) blue
(G) green
(R) red
(Y) yellow

Peter

Doris

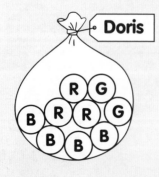

a. What is the probability that Emily picks a red marble?

_____

b. What is the probability that Peter picks a green marble?

_____

c. What is the probability that Doris picks a blue marble?

_____

d. A child said, "The probability that I will pick a green marble is 0." Who said this?

_____

e. Who has the greatest chance of picking a blue marble?

_____

Spin and Win

② The Fisher King Bistro is holding a "Spin and Win" event. For every $10 spent, a customer can spin one of the spinners once to try to win a prize.

a. For Spinner A, what is the probability of landing on "Hamburger"?

_____

b. For Spinner B, what is the probability of landing on "Sandwich"?

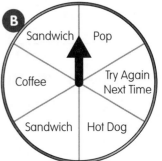

_____

c. For Spinner C, what is the probability of landing on "Pop"?

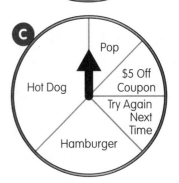

_____

d. Which spinner has the greatest probability of landing on "Hot Dog"? What is the probability?

_____

e. Which spinner has the smallest probability of landing on "Try Again Next Time"? What is the probability?

_____

f.

> I spent $20 so I get 2 spins on the same spinner. If I want to win a hot dog or a hamburger, which spinner should I choose? What is the probability of landing on either prize?

_____

Read the table about the students in Mr. Keller's class and answer the questions.

③ Mr. Keller wants to choose a student to clean the chalkboard. What is the probability that

a. a boy with glasses is picked?

_____

b. a girl without glasses is picked?

_____

Description		No. of Students
Boys	with glasses	2
	without glasses	10
Girls	with glasses	1
	without glasses	7

④ One of the students missed a class. What is the probability that the student was a girl?

_____

Draw a tree diagram to show all the possible outcomes. Then find the probabilities.

⑤ Alex has a coin and a bag with 1 red, 1 yellow, and 1 blue marble. His sister flips the coin and takes a marble from the bag.

Coin	Marble	Combination

a. How many possible outcomes are there?

_____

b. What is the probability that she will get tails and a blue marble?

_____

c. Are all the possible outcomes equally likely? Explain.

_____

_____

_____

Grade 5
QR Code

QR Code – a quick way to access our fun-filled videos

Our QR code provides you with a quick and easy link to our fun-filled videos, which can help enrich your learning experience while you are working on the workbook. Below is a summary of the topics that the QR code brings you to. You may scan the QR code in each unit to learn about the topic or the QR code on the right to review all the topics you have learned in this book.

Scan this QR code or visit our Download Centre at *www.popularbook.ca*.

The topics introduced with the QR code:

1 **How to Divide** (p. 11)
Watch how a 3-digit number is divided by a 1-digit number with a remainder.

2 **The 3 Types of Fractions** (p. 43)
Learn to differentiate between proper fractions, improper fractions, and mixed numbers.

3 **Converting between Improper Fractions and Mixed Numbers** (p. 45)
Discover how improper fractions and mixed numbers are related.

4 **Thermometers** (p. 51)
Explore thermometers and their uses.

5 **Nets of Solids** (p. 71)
Investigate the nets that make different solids.

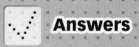

Level 1

1 Whole Numbers

Try It

20 000 + 5000 + 70 + 9
twenty-five thousand seventy-nine

1. 30 000 + 5000 + 500 + 60 + 3 ; thirty-five thousand five hundred sixty-three
2. 90 000 + 900 + 20 + 1 ; ninety thousand nine hundred twenty-one
3. 46 214 ; forty-six thousand two hundred fourteen
4. 70 629 ; 70 000 + 600 + 20 + 9
5. 84 010 ; eighty-four thousand ten
6. 10　　　　　　　7. 4000
8. 6000　　　　　　9. 300
10. 2　　　　　　　11. 90 000
12. 20 000　　　　　13. 2
14. 0　　　　　　　15. 80
16. A: 56 359　　　　B: 91 670
　　C: 43 786　　　　D: 52 914
　　E: 68 103　　　　F: 87 795
　　G: 64 059　　　　H: 95 046
　　I: 59 082　　　　J: 47 301
17. G　　　　　　　18. hundreds
19. J　　　　　　　20. ones
21. F ; J　　　　　　22. 82 522 ; 85 200
23. 97 945 ; 97 109　　24. 68 329 ; 68 293
25. 43 876 ; 48 341
26. 45 992 < 48 806 < 49 999
27. 93 159 < 94 120 < 94 126
28. 84 943 < 85 967 < 88 779
29. 18 656 < 18 837 < 19 586
30. 72 578 < 75 113 < 75 967
31. 30 278 < 30 355 < 30 606
32. $33 454 < $34 202 < $34 513 < $35 255 < $35 314
33. 50 000　　　　　34. 20 000
35. 20 000　　　　　36. 40 000
37. 80 000

38.

	ten thousands	thousands	hundreds	tens
43 509	40 000	44 000	43 500	43 510
76 168	80 000	76 000	76 200	76 170
52 945	50 000	53 000	52 900	52 950
13 999	10 000	14 000	14 000	14 000
24 547	20 000	25 000	24 500	24 550

39a. 13 479　　　　　b. 97 431
　c. (Suggested answer) 31 479
40a. (Suggested answer) 13 259
　b. 12 539　　　　　c. 52 913

2 Multiplying and Dividing Whole Numbers

Try It

```
    42
 x  79
   378
  2940
  3318
```

1.
```
    84
 x  34
   336
  2520
  2856
```

2.
```
    68
 x  42
   136
  2720
  2856
```

3.
```
    15
 x  89
   135
  1200
  1335
```

4.
```
    45
 x  37
   315
  1350
  1665
```

5.
```
    71
 x  62
   142
  4260
  4402
```

6.
```
    39
 x  54
   156
  1950
  2106
```

7.
```
    83
 x  24
   332
  1660
  1992
```

8.
```
    57
 x  16
   342
   570
   912
```

9.
```
    28
 x  28
   224
   560
   784
```

10. 384
```
    16
 x  24
    64
   320
   384
```

11. 735
```
    21
 x  35
   105
   630
   735
```

12. 1204
```
    43
 x  28
   344
   860
  1204
```

13. 636
```
    12
 x  53
    36
   600
   636
```

14. 1798
```
    29
 x  62
    58
  1740
  1798
```

15. 1504
```
    32
 x  47
   224
  1280
  1504
```

16.
```
    39
  x 72
  ────
    78
  2730
  ────
  2808
```
40 ; 70 ; 2800

17.
```
    28
  x 91
  ────
    28
  2520
  ────
  2548
```
30 ; 90 ; 2700

18.
```
      134
   2)268
      2
      ─
      6
      6
      ─
      8
      8
      ─
```

19.
```
      213
   4)852
      8
      ─
      5
      4
      ─
      12
      12
      ──
```

20.
```
      188
   5)940
      5
      ─
      44
      40
      ──
      40
      40
      ──
```

21.
```
      312
   3)936
      9
      ─
      3
      3
      ─
      6
      6
      ─
```

22.
```
      43R1
   4)173
      16
      ──
      13
      12
      ──
      1
```

23.
```
      102R4
   6)616
      6
      ─
      16
      12
      ──
      4
```

24.
```
      341R1
   2)683
      6
      ─
      8
      8
      ─
      3
      2
      ─
      1
```

25.
```
      65R5
   8)525
      48
      ──
      45
      40
      ──
      5
```

26.
```
      57R5
   7)404
      35
      ──
      54
      49
      ──
      5
```

27. A: 72R2
```
      72R2
   3)218
      21
      ──
      8
      6
      ─
      2
```

B: 71
```
      71
   7)497
      49
      ──
      7
      7
      ─
```

C: 15R4
```
      15R4
   8)124
      8
      ─
      44
      40
      ──
      4
```

D: 218R2
```
      218R2
   4)874
      8
      ─
      7
      4
      ─
      34
      32
      ──
      2
```

E: 157R1
```
      157R1
   3)472
      3
      ─
      17
      15
      ──
      22
      21
      ──
      1
```

F: 83R2
```
      83R2
   6)500
      48
      ──
      20
      18
      ──
      2
```

G: 99R2
```
      99R2
   7)695
      63
      ──
      65
      63
      ──
      2
```

H: 167R2
```
      167R2
   5)837
      5
      ─
      33
      30
      ──
      37
      35
      ──
      2
```

28.

A 2	G 1	0	
B 5	2		C 3	0
	D 2	0	7	0
E 4		F 7	5	0
6		6	

3 Decimals

Try It

3.27 ; 3 and 27 hundredths

1. 3.04 ; 3 and 4 hundredths
2. 1.7 ; 1 and 70 hundredths/1 and 7 tenths
3. 2.4 ; 2 and 40 hundredths/2 and 4 tenths
4. 0.73 ; 73 hundredths
5. 4.69 ; 4 and 69 hundredths
6. 1.31 ; 1 and 31 hundredths

7.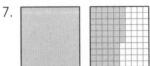

8.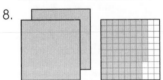

9.

10.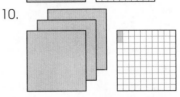

11. 0.5
12. 0.07
13. 20
14. 3
15. 0.06
16. 0.01
17. 0.09
18. 0.7
19. 1.2, 1.20
20. 3.10, 3.1
21. 0.8, 0.80
22. 2.50, 2.5
23. 4.0, 4.00
24. 2.00, 2
25. <
26. >
27. >
28. >
29. <
30. >
31. <
32. >
33. <
34. <
35. >
36. <
37. >
38. >
39. <
40. 0.15 < 0.2 < 0.24 < 0.3

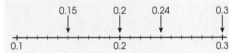

41. 0.6 < 0.65 < 0.75 < 0.9

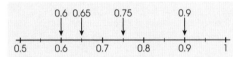

42. 0.78 < 0.8 < 0.82 < 0.88

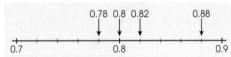

43. 1.4 ; 1.45 ; 1.5 ; 1.54
44. 3.2 ; 2.93 ; 2.9 ; 2.09
45. 0.39 ; 0.73 ; 0.79 ; 0.97
46. 5.51 ; 5.5 ; 5.15 ; 5.05
47. 2.1

```
     2.12
      ↓
  +--+--+--+--+--+--+
  2.1              2.2
```

48. 3.1

```
        3.07
         ↓
  +--+--+--+--+--+
  3              3.1
```

49. 0.4

```
           0.39
            ↓
  +--+--+--+--+--+
  0.3            0.4
```

50. 5.3

```
        5.27
         ↓
  +--+--+--+--+--+
  5.2            5.3
```

51. 4.4

```
          4.39
           ↓
  +--+--+--+--+--+
  4.3            4.4
```

52. 12.1

```
      12.14
        ↓
  +--+--+--+--+--+
  12.1           12.2
```

53. one: 2 ; 2 ; 5 ; 4 ; 1
    tenth: 1.6 ; 2.4 ; 5.1 ; 3.8 ; 0.9
54-56. (Suggested answers)
54. 2.58
55. 4.53
56. 5.08

4 Adding Decimals

Try It
5.79
1. 1.5
2. 10.68
3. 9.82
4. 8.01
5. 12.93
6. 13.87
7. 28.21
8. 34.23
9. 30.91
10. 37.14
11. 28.83
12. 58.10
13. 56.40
14. 26.00
15. 58.01
16. 26.23
17. 12.96
```
      5.14
   +  7.82
   ------
     12.96
```
18. 7.69
```
      6.91
   +  0.78
   ------
      7.69
```
19. 7.63
```
      2.73
   +  4.90
   ------
      7.63
```
20. 8.23
```
      7.00
   +  1.23
   ------
      8.23
```
21. 14.63
```
      5.90
   +  8.73
   ------
     14.63
```
22. 9.93
```
      7.03
   +  2.90
   ------
      9.93
```
23. 52.57
```
     11.67
   + 40.90
   ------
     52.57
```
24. 29.15
```
     22.45
   +  6.70
   ------
     29.15
```
25. 62.13
```
     52.93
   +  9.20
   ------
     62.13
```
26. 91.82
```
     89.00
   +  2.82
   ------
     91.82
```
27. 67.45
```
     41.05
   + 26.40
   ------
     67.45
```
28. 52.42
```
     17.42
   + 35.00
   ------
     52.42
```
29.

		Sum
2.09	12.47	16.54
7.63	7.02	14.56
8.24	8.3	15.64
9.88	5.76	14.65
9.22	6.24	15.46

30. 10.27 ; 10

31. 11.17 ;
```
   10
+   1
   11
```

32. 11.32 ;
```
   5
+  6
   11
```

33. 11.14 ;
```
   11
+   0
   11
```

34. 85.83 ;
```
   71
    4
+  11
   86
```

35. 75.00 ;
```
   30
   40
+   5
   75
```

36.
```
   19.99
+ 25.45
   45.44
```
$45.44

37.
```
   1.70
+ 0.88
   2.58
```
2.58 L

38.
```
   3.75
+ 2.05
   5.80
```
5.8 kg

39.
```
   0.32
+ 1.09
   1.41
```
1.41 GB

40.
```
   2.35
+ 1.38
   3.73
```
3.73 km

41.
```
   905.25
+ 620.70
  1525.95
```
1525.95 g

42.
```
   1.25
+ 2.20
   3.45
```
3.45 h

43.
```
    58.77
+ 102.29
   161.06
```
$161.06

44.
```
   386.81
+ 134.07
   520.88
```
520.88 g

45.
```
   236.60
+ 145.52
   382.12
```
382.12 mL

46.
```
   2.82
+ 5.34
   8.16
```
8.16 min

47.
```
   570.68
+ 256.29
   826.97
```
826.97 cm

48.
```
   12.73
+  8.06
   20.79
```
$20.79K

49.
```
   2.93
+ 1.78
   4.71
```
4.71 million people

5 Subtracting Decimals

Try It

2.55

1. 0.5
2. 6.5
3. 6.29
4. 1.18
5. 8.44
6. 3.78
7. 5.04
8. 8.69
9. 3.06
10. 15.16
11. 23.71
12. 45.15
13. 3.88
14. 1.93
15. 8.76
16. 13.29

17. 1.98
18. 5.03
19. 3.77
20. 8.27
21. 3.02
22. 11.38
23. 7.87
24. 1.82
25. 0.88
26. 0.22
27. 0.26
28. 0.81
29. 2.34
30. 0.06
31. 32.47
32. 26.38
33. 20.77
34. 12.05
35. 19.78
36. 1.59
37. 1.4
38. 8
39. 3.36
40. 2.4
41. 2
42. 2.61
43. 4.2
44. 1.23
45. 0.65
46. 7.7
47. 7.38
48. 2.45
49. 7.49
50. 9.46

1

2.19	5.07	3.36		
5.4	2	1.23		
1.01	4.01	7.38	5	3.68
0.87	5	4.2	0.9	3
4.8	6.28	8	6.5	1.21
2.22	3.13	0.65	4.97	0.29
3.6	1.88	2.4	3.46	8.7
0.7	5.9	7.7	0.61	10
7.49	9.46	1.4	2.61	2.45

51. 5.17 ; 5

52. 7.76 ;
```
   27
-  19
    8
```

53. 5.73 ;
```
   33
-  28
    5
```

54. 18.87 ;
```
   81
-  62
   19
```

55. 1.62 ;
```
   21
-  20
    1
```

56. 38.41 ;
```
   55
-  17
   38
```

57.
```
   850.0
- 236.6
   613.4
```
613.4 mL

58.
```
   360.88
- 199.99
   160.89
```
$160.89

59.
```
   28.36
- 21.87
    6.49
```
6.49 km

60.
```
   2.00
- 0.31
   1.69
```
1.69 kg

6 Multiplying Decimals

Try It
43.2 ; 432 ; 4320

1. 4 ; 40 ; 400
2. 0.2 ; 2 ; 20
3. 1.2 ; 12 ; 120
4. 39 ; 390 ; 3900
5. 25 ; 250 ; 2500
6. 10.4 ; 104 ; 1040
7. 63.9 ; 639 ; 6390
8. 74.2 ; 742 ; 7420
9. $2.60   10. $51
11. 51 200 g   12. 432 g
13. 75 L   14. 1985 mL
15a. 2800 cm   b. 610 cm
  c. 143 cm
16a. $160   b. $250
  c. $381.20
17a. 146 kg   b. 2.8 kg
  c. 130 kg
18. 46 ; 52.1 ; 30.9
19. 128 ; 7 ; 641
20. 300 ; 1460 ; 8010
21. 0.32 ; 0.58 ; 1.07
22. 0.03 ; 0.4 ; 2.1
23. 0.07 ; 0.81 ; 0.09
24a. 10 ; 100 ; 10 ; 1000
  b. 10   c. 1000
  d. 10   e. 10
  f. 1000   g. 1000
25. 10 ; 6   26. 2 ; 1.8
                      10 ; 1.8
                      18
27. $= 2 \times 5 \times 3.86$ 28. $= 1.77 \times 100$
    $= 10 \times 3.86$ $= 177$
    $= 38.6$
29. $= 20 \times 5 \times 6.14$ 30. $= 50 \times 2 \times 0.49$
    $= 100 \times 6.14$ $= 100 \times 0.49$
    $= 614$ $= 49$
31. $= 8.2 \times 10$ 32. $= 200 \times 5 \times 1.99$
    $= 82$ $= 1000 \times 1.99$
                                      $= 1990$
33. $= 26.3 \times 1000$
    $= 26\ 300$
34. 82   35. 39 270
36. 23   37. 563
38. 1220   39. 162
40. 18 050   41. 6500
    (Individual time)

7 Dividing Decimals

Try It
0.623 ; 0.0623 ; 0.00623

1a. 9.8   b. 0.98
  c. 0.098
2a. 0.5   b. 0.05
  c. 0.005
3a. 0.07   b. 0.007
  c. 0.0007
4a. 0.205   b. 0.0205
  c. 0.00205
5. 0.28   6. 0.316
7. 0.014   8. 0.04
9. 0.16   10. 0.008
11. 0.31   12. 0.00256
13. 0.044   14. 0.0118
15. 0.0009   16. 0.9
17. 2.5   18. 0.0092
19a. 26 ; 2.6
  b. $26 \div 100 = 0.26$ (kg)
20a. $450 \div 100 = 4.5$ (km)
  b. $450 \div 1000 = 0.45$ (km)
21a. $913 \div 100 = 9.13$ (L)
  b. $913 \div 1000 = 0.913$ (L)
22a. $\$580 \div 10 = \$58$
  b. $\$580 \div 100 = \$5.80$
23a. $1250 \div 10 = 125$ (cm)
  b. $1250 \div 100 = 12.5$ (cm)
24a. $38 \div 10 = 3.8$ (kg)
  b. $38 \div 100 = 0.38$ (kg)
25.   ; 7

Math Quiz   Name: _Sam_

1. $20.1 \div 10 =$ _2.1_ (✗) 2.01
2. $399 \div 100 =$ _3.99_ (✓)
3. $4500 \div 1000 =$ _0.45_ (✗) 4.5
4. $825 \div 100 =$ _8.25_ (✓)
5. $4.7 \div 10 =$ _0.47_ (✓)
6. $250 \div 1000 =$ _2.05_ (✗) 0.25
7. $36 \div 100 =$ _0.36_ (✓)
8. $60.8 \div 10 =$ _6.08_ (✓)
9. $13 \div 100 =$ _1.3_ (✗) 0.13
10. $5020 \div 1000 =$ _5.02_ (✓)
11. $1240 \div 1000 =$ _12.4_ (✗) 1.24
12. $16.8 \div 100 =$ _1.68_ (✗) 0.168
13. $40.5 \div 100 =$ _4.05_ (✗) 0.405
14. $840 \div 10 =$ _84_ (✓)

26. 10   27. 100
28. 1000   29. 100
30. 10   31. 100
32. 100   33. 100
34. 100   35. 10
36. 1000   37. 1000
38. 10   39. 1000

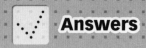

40. 15.8   41. 62.
42. 0.37   43. 5.4
44. 0.052   45. 1680.
46. 4.2   47. 0.8
48. 3.2   49. 2400.
50. 61.   51. 9.
52. 41.3   53. 0.302
54. 0.06

8 Fractions

Try It
$\frac{4}{5}$; $\frac{1}{2}$

1. $\frac{1}{6}$; $\frac{5}{6}$ 2. $\frac{2}{4}$; $\frac{2}{4}$
3. $\frac{5}{8}$; $\frac{3}{8}$ 4. $\frac{2}{5}$; $\frac{3}{5}$
5. $\frac{6}{10}$; $\frac{4}{10}$ 6. $\frac{11}{24}$; $\frac{13}{24}$

7. A: 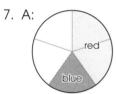   B:

C: 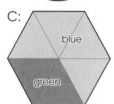   D: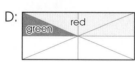

E:

8. 2 ; 3   9. 3 ; 1
10. 5 ; 1   11. 2 ; 1
12.   13.

14.    15.

16. A ; C   17. A ; C
18. A   19. 2
20. 2   21. 2
22. 4   23. 6
24. 5   25. 6
26. 10   27. 8

9 Ordering Fractions

Try It
$\frac{3}{4}$

1a. $\boxed{\frac{1}{4}}$; $\frac{2}{4}$ b. $\boxed{\frac{1}{3}}$; $\frac{2}{3}$
   c. $\frac{3}{4}$; $\boxed{\frac{1}{4}}$

2a. $\frac{2}{4}$; $\boxed{\frac{3}{4}}$ b. $\frac{2}{5}$; $\boxed{\frac{4}{5}}$
   c. $\frac{3}{5}$; $\boxed{\frac{4}{5}}$

3. 2 ; <   4. 2 ; 3 ; >
5. 2 ; 4 ; <   6. 1 ; 3 ; 5 ; <
7. 3 ; 5 ; >
8a. $\frac{1}{8} < \frac{4}{8} < \frac{5}{8}$ b. $\frac{1}{6} < \frac{2}{6} < \frac{5}{6}$
   c. $\frac{3}{7} < \frac{6}{7} < \frac{7}{7}$

9a. $\frac{8}{10} > \frac{5}{10} > \frac{3}{10}$ b. $\frac{10}{12} > \frac{8}{12} > \frac{7}{12}$
   c. $\frac{4}{9} > \frac{2}{9} > \frac{1}{9}$

10. $\frac{5}{10}$; $\frac{7}{10}$; $\frac{3}{10}$
   $\frac{7}{10}$; $\frac{5}{10}$; $\frac{3}{10}$

11. $\frac{4}{6}$; $\frac{2}{6}$; $\frac{1}{6}$
   $\frac{4}{6}$; $\frac{2}{6}$; $\frac{1}{6}$

12. $\frac{3}{8}$; $\frac{4}{8}$; $\frac{5}{8}$
   $\frac{5}{8}$; $\frac{4}{8}$; $\frac{3}{8}$

13. $\frac{3}{5}$; $\frac{1}{5}$; $\frac{2}{5}$
   $\frac{3}{5}$; $\frac{2}{5}$; $\frac{1}{5}$

14. $\frac{4}{5}$ $\boxed{\frac{2}{5}}$ $\boxed{\frac{1}{5}}$ 15. $\boxed{\frac{5}{7}}$ $\frac{3}{7}$ $\boxed{\frac{6}{7}}$

16. $\boxed{\frac{5}{8}}$ $\frac{1}{8}$ $\boxed{\frac{6}{8}}$ 17. $\boxed{\frac{5}{6}}$ $\frac{3}{6}$ $\boxed{\frac{1}{6}}$

18-27. (Suggested answers)

18. 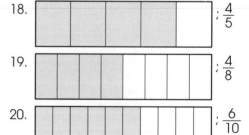 ; $\frac{4}{5}$

19. ; $\frac{4}{8}$

20. ; $\frac{6}{10}$

21.  ; $\frac{6}{7}$

22. ; $\frac{3}{6}$

23. ; $\frac{5}{9}$

24. ; $\frac{3}{12}$

25. ; $\frac{7}{11}$

26. ; $\frac{7}{13}$

27. ; $\frac{11}{14}$

10 Improper Fractions and Mixed Numbers

Try It

mixed number ; proper fraction ; improper fraction

1. Proper Fraction: $\frac{2}{6}$; $\frac{5}{7}$; $\frac{10}{12}$; $\frac{1}{3}$

   Improper Fraction: $\frac{5}{2}$; $\frac{8}{8}$; $\frac{4}{3}$; $\frac{9}{6}$

   Mixed Number: $1\frac{1}{2}$; $3\frac{1}{4}$; $2\frac{2}{3}$; $1\frac{1}{6}$

   Improper fractions and mixed numbers are greater than one.

2. $\frac{4}{3}$; $1\frac{1}{3}$ 3. $\frac{6}{4}$; $1\frac{2}{4}$

4. $\frac{7}{6}$; $1\frac{1}{6}$ 5. $\frac{15}{8}$; $1\frac{7}{8}$

6. $\frac{8}{5}$; $1\frac{3}{5}$ 7. $\frac{5}{2}$; $2\frac{1}{2}$

8. $\frac{8}{3}$; $2\frac{2}{3}$ 9. $\frac{11}{4}$; $2\frac{3}{4}$

10. $\frac{14}{4}$; $3\frac{2}{4}$ 11. $\frac{32}{9}$; $3\frac{5}{9}$

12. $4\frac{1}{2}$

```
    4R1
  2)9
    8
    1
```

13. $3\frac{3}{4}$

```
    3R3
  4)15
    12
    3
```

14. $3\frac{2}{5}$

```
      3R2
  5)17
    15
    2
```

15. $1\frac{3}{7}$

```
      1R3
  7)10
    7
    3
```

16. $2\frac{2}{3}$ 17. $2\frac{1}{4}$

18. $2\frac{2}{5}$ 19. $2\frac{3}{4}$

20. $3\frac{1}{5}$ 21. $2\frac{3}{8}$

22. $2\frac{3}{7}$ 23. $3\frac{1}{3}$

24. ✔   25. ✗ ; $3\frac{1}{2}$

26. ✔   27. ✗ ; $2\frac{4}{5}$

28. ✗ ; $2\frac{5}{8}$ 29. ✗ ; $2\frac{1}{7}$

30. $\frac{2 \times 7 + 1}{7}$; $\frac{15}{7}$

31. $\frac{3 \times 8 + 5}{8}$; $\frac{29}{8}$

32. $\frac{3 \times 3 + 1}{3}$; $\frac{10}{3}$

33. $\frac{1 \times 6 + 5}{6}$; $\frac{11}{6}$

34. $\frac{17}{4}$ 35. $\frac{11}{2}$

36. $\frac{17}{5}$ 37. $\frac{10}{7}$

38. $\frac{17}{5}$ 39. $\frac{13}{6}$

40. $\frac{13}{4}$ 41. $\frac{17}{8}$

42. 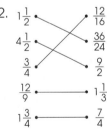   43.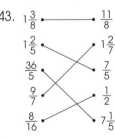

11 Fractions and Decimals

Try It

$\frac{1}{4}$; 0.25

1.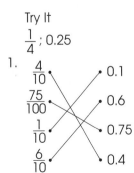

2.

3.

4.

5.

6.

7.

8. $\frac{3}{10}$; 0.3

9. $\frac{7}{10}$; 0.7

10. $\frac{33}{100}$; 0.33

11. $\frac{53}{100}$; 0.53

12. $\frac{67}{100}$; 0.67

13. $\frac{89}{100}$; 0.89

14. $\frac{91}{100}$; 0.91

15a. 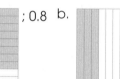 ; 0.8 b. ; 0.3

c. ; 0.42 d. ; 0.67

16a.  ; $\frac{7}{10}$ b. ; $\frac{9}{10}$

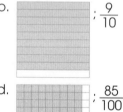

c.  ; $\frac{31}{100}$ d. ; $\frac{85}{100}$

17a. 0.1

b. 0.6

c. $\frac{2}{10}$

d. $\frac{5}{10}$

e. 0.43

f. $\frac{19}{100}$

g. $\frac{77}{100}$

h. 0.87

i. $\frac{55}{100}$

j. 0.35

k. $\frac{16}{100}$

l. 0.5

m. 0.4

n. $\frac{22}{100}$

18. < 19. > 20. < 21. >

22. = 23. = 24. < 25. =

26. < 27. = 28. = 29. >

12 Time and Temperature

Try It

7:20:45

1. 10:40:50

2. 4:05:25

3. 12:25:10

4. 2:30:40

5. 5:50:00

6. 6:20:30

7.

8.

9a. 07:00

b. 09:46

c. 16:00

d. 20:37

e. 22:08

f. 11:36

10a. 10:00 a.m.

b. 2:08 a.m.

c. 1:21 p.m.

d. 3:26 p.m.

e. 9:54 p.m.

f. 11:39 p.m.

11a. 10:36:20 a.m. ; C

b. 8:45:15 p.m. ; B

c. 5:21:19 a.m. ; D

d. 9:50:03 p.m. ; A

12. A: 5° below 0°C   B: 20° below 0°C

C: 15° below 0°C D: 10°C

13.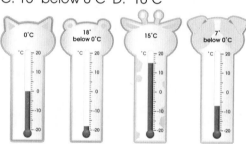

14. 20 ; dropped ; 35

15. 5 ; below ; 3

16. 10 ; below ; 5

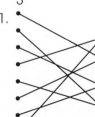

13 Length and Perimeter

Try It

3

1.

2. A: 14 cm   B: 9 cm
   C: 12 cm   D: 11 cm
   E: 15 cm
3. (Draw a 15-cm line.)
4. (Draw a 13-cm line.)
5. (Draw an 8-cm line.)
6. (Draw a 12-cm line.)
7. 20   8. 480
9. 1900   10. 7.5
11. 700   12. 5
13. 6000   14. 30
15. 0.2   16. 4.2
17. 3000   18. 8200
19. A: 30   B: 20 km
    C: 20 cm   D: 40 m
    E: 118 mm   F: 75 m
20a. 3 ; 12   b. 4 x 5 ; 20 (cm)
21a. 2 ; 1 ; 6
    b. 2 x 9 + 2 x 3 ; 24 (cm)
22. A: 24 cm   B: 16 m
    C: 28 km   D: 18 mm

14   Area

Try It
9 cm²
1. 5 ; 9 cm² ; 11 cm² ; 10 cm² ; 8 cm²
2. 3 ; 3 ; 9   3. 5 x 5 = 25 (cm²)
4. 4 x 4 = 16 (m²)   5. 8 x 8 = 64 (mm²)
6. 7 x 7 = 49 (cm²)
7. A: 9 cm²   B: 36 cm²
   C: 16 cm²   D: 25 cm²
   E: 4 cm²
8. 6 ; 3 ; 18   9. 14 x 5 = 70 (mm²)
10. 18 x 3 = 54 (km²)   11. 9 x 7 = 63 (m²)
12. 16 x 6 = 96 (cm²)   13. 20 x 4 = 80 (mm²)
14. 35 x 19 = 665 (m²)
15. 70 x 52 = 3640 (km²)
16. A: 11 ; 3 ; 33 cm²
    B: 10 cm by 4 cm ; 40 cm²
    C: 7 cm by 2 cm ; 14 cm²
    D: 8 cm by 8 cm ; 64 cm²
    E: 5 cm by 5 cm ; 25 cm²
    F: 8 cm by 4 cm ; 32 cm²

15   Volume and Capacity

Try It
16 cm³

1. A: 24   B: 16 cm³
   C: 6 cm³   D: 27 cm³
   E: 12 cm³   F: 12 cm³
   G: 8 cm³
2. A: 15 ; 4 ; 60   B: 24 ; 4 ; 96
   C: 12 ; 5 ; 60   D: 4 ; 5 ; 20
   E: 9 ; 6 ; 54
   multiplied
3. 6 ; 5 ; 3 ; 90
4. 8 x 6 x 2 ; 96 (cm³)
5. 1500 cm³   6. 100 cm³
7. 3000 cm³   8. 1440 cm³
9. 2240 cm³   10. 2160 cm³
11. A: 30 ; 14 ; 5 ; 2100 ; 2100
    B: 8 x 12 x 8 ; 768 (cm³) ; 768 (mL)
    C: 11 x 4 x 1 ; 44 (cm³) ; 44 (mL)
12. 100 ; 100
13. 250 ; 250
14. 30 ; 30 ; 5 ; 4500 ; 4500

16   Angles and Triangles

Try It
120° ; obtuse angle
1. A: 90 ° ; right angle
   B: 50° ; acute angle
   C: 130° ; obtuse angle
   D: 180° ; straight angle
   E: 75° ; acute angle
   F: 140° ; obtuse angle
   G: 180° ; straight angle
2.

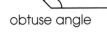

acute angle   obtuse angle

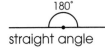

right angle   straight angle

3. (Suggested drawings)

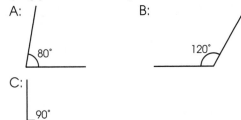

A: B:

C:

4. acute triangle   5. obtuse triangle
6. right triangle   7. obtuse triangle

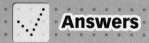

8. 60° ; 60° ; 60° ; acute triangle
9. 50° ; 90° ; 40° ; right triangle
10. 40° ; 120° ; 20° ; obtuse triangle
11. 90° ; 55° ; 35° ; right triangle
12. isosceles triangle
13. equilateral triangle
14. scalene triangle
15. isosceles triangle
16. right triangle ; scalene triangle

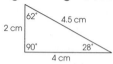

17. right triangle ; isosceles triangle

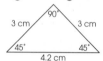

18. obtuse triangle ; scalene triangle

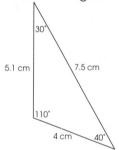

17 Shapes and Solids

Try It

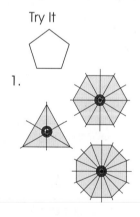

1.

A: parallelogram ; 4 ; 4
B: hexagon ; 6 ; 6
C: triangle ; 3 ; 3
D: octagon ; 8 ; 8
E: rhombus ; 4 ; 4
F: trapezoid ; 4 ; 4
G: triangle ; 3 ; 3
Yes

2. square   3. trapezoid
4. 3 ; 2 ; flat   5. 8 ; 12 ; 6 ; cube
6. 6 ; 10 ; 6 ; pentagonal pyramid
7. 12 ; 18 ; 8 ; hexagonal prism
8. 5 ; 8 ; 5 ; rectangular pyramid
9.

No. of Vertices	4	5	6	7
No. of Edges	6	8	10	12
No. of Faces	4	5	6	7
No. of Triangular Faces (excluding the base)	3	4	5	6
Shape of Base	triangle	square	pentagon	hexagon

a. vertices ; faces   b. triangular faces
c. edges   d. one
10a. triangular pyramid
b. cube   c. hexagonal pyramid
d. triangular prism   e. rectangular prism
11.

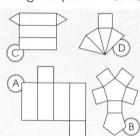

12. cube   13. rectangular prism
14. triangular prism
15. square-based pyramid
16. triangular pyramid
17. hexagonal pyramid

18 Coordinate Systems

Try It
north ; east

1.

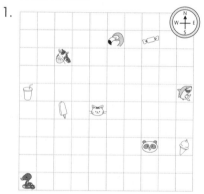

2a. D1   3.
b. H1
c. G5
d. C3
e. B4
f. E4
g. A7
h. C6
i. G3
j. F6
k. E2
l. D7
4a. 2 fruits
b. 3 fruits
c. 2 fruits

5. B6
6. B5
7. west
8. north
9. 3 ; 3
10. 3 ; 1
11. 4 blocks south ;
    1 block east
12a. south ; west
  b. Move 5 blocks south
     and 4 blocks west.
  c. Move 4 blocks north
     and 1 block west.
  d. Move 5 blocks north
     and 2 blocks east.
13. Move 6 blocks north and 2 blocks east.
14. Move 5 blocks north and 3 blocks west.
15. Lucy   16. Sam
17. Jessie   18. Alex
19. He moves 2 blocks north and 3 blocks east
    to reach the park. Then he moves 3 blocks
    north and 1 block west to reach home.

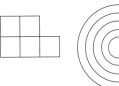

19 Transformations

Try It

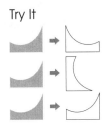

1. reflection   2. translation
3. rotation   4. reflection
5. translation   6. rotation
7. 3 ; right ; 3 ; down
8. 3 units to the left and 3 units down
9. A to V: 4 units to the right and 1 unit down
   A to W: 10 units to the right
   A to X: 4 units down
   A to Y: 7 units to the right and 3 units down
   A to Z: 12 units to the right and 4 units down
10.

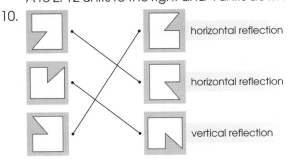

horizontal reflection

horizontal reflection

vertical reflection

11. 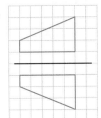   12.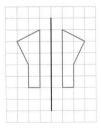

13. the same 14. A   15. A
16. A   17. B
18. $\frac{1}{4}$ turn clockwise / $\frac{3}{4}$ turn counterclockwise

    $\frac{1}{2}$ turn

    $\frac{1}{4}$ turn counterclockwise / $\frac{3}{4}$ turn clockwise

    $\frac{1}{4}$ turn counterclockwise / $\frac{3}{4}$ turn clockwise

20 Patterning

Try It
A ; C

1.

Growing Pattern(s): B, C
Shrinking Pattern(s): A
2. 64 ; 128 ; growing
3. 2 ; 0 ; shrinking
4. 44 ; 132 ; growing
5. 9 ; 3 ; shrinking
6. 46 ; 47 ; growing
7. A   8. B   9. A   10. B
11. 102 ; 103
    Start at 11. Add 1. Then multiply by 2.
12. 13 ; 12
    Start at 111. Subtract 1. Then divide by 2.
13. 97 ; 291
    Start at 6. Multiply by 3. Then subtract 5.
14. 7 ; 10
    Start at 35. Add 3. Then divide by 2.
15. 4 ; 2
    Start at 88. Divide by 2. Then subtract 4.
16.

17. 26 ; 20 ; 21 ; 15 ; 16 ; PIGLETS
18. 50 ; 45 ; 9 ; 4 ; DUCKS
19. 9 ; 6 ; 24 ; COWS
20. 1 ; 6 ; 3 ; 18 ; 15 ; HORSES

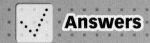

21 Simple Equations

Try It

5

1-5. (Individual guess-and-check)

1. 7
2. 4
3. 5
4. 10
5. 8
6. 4
7. 5
8. 10

○ ○ ○ ⊗   ○ ○ ○ ○ ○
⊗ ⊗ ⊗ ⊗   ○ ○ ⊗ ⊗ ⊗

9. 4
10. 7

○ ○ ○ ○   ○ ○ ○ ○ ○ ⊗
○ ○ ○ ○ ○   ⊗ ⊗ ⊗ ⊗ ⊗ ⊗ ⊗

11. 2
12. 3

13. 8
14. 2

15. 4
16. 13
17. 4
18. 30
19. 8
20. 41
21. 19

(Individual time)

22. 6
23. 72
24. 9
25. 8
26. 8
27. 3
28. 4

(Individual time)

29. 70
30. 8
31. 12
32. 81
33. 36
34. 13
35. 26
36. 28

honeydew

37. 3
38. 20
39. 49
40. 22
41. 24
42. 25
43. 32
44. 7

eggplant

22 Mean, Median, and Mode

Try It

$(5 + 4 + 10 + 5) ÷ 4 = 6$

1. A: $(11 + 5 + 6 + 10) ÷ 4 = 8$
   B: $(5 + 9 + 4 + 7 + 8 + 3) ÷ 6 = 6$
   C: $(4 + 6 + 10 + 7 + 8) ÷ 5 = 7$
   D: $(9 + 8 + 4 + 6 + 3 + 7 + 12) ÷ 7 = 7$

2a. A
   b. B
   c. no
   d. no

3. Mean: $(8 + 11 + 12 + 12 + 16 + 19) ÷ 6 = 13$
   Median: 12
   Mode: 12

4. Mean: $(11 + 15 + 28 + 32 + 32 + 32) ÷ 6 = 25$
   Median: 30
   Mode: 32

5. 7 ; 7 years old ; 8 years old
6. 18 ; 18 lollipops ; 18 lollipops
7. 18 ; 18 apples ; 12, 16, and 20 apples
8. 20 ; 21 cm ; 22 cm

9a. $6 ; $6 ; $4   b. $5 ; $5 ; $5

10a. $76 \times 5 - 78 - 86 - 92 - 68 = 56$; 56
   b. $77 \times 5 - 78 - 86 - 92 - 68 = 61$; 61

11. A, B, C, and D   12. A, B, C, and E

13.

	Week 1	Week 2	Week 3	Week 4
Mean	112 s	113 s	108 s	106 s
Median	110 s	110 s	106 s	104 s
Mode	105 s	110 s	106 s	104 s

14. C   15. A
16. B

23 Probability

Try It

X, Y, Z

1. 1, 2, 3, 4, 5, 6, 7   2. W, X, Y, Z
3. 1, 2, 3, 4, 5, 6   4. A, B, C, D
5. B ; 1, 2, 3, 4   6. A ; A, B
7. A ; P, Q
8. 4 red balls, 4 green balls
9. 2 As, 2 Bs, 2 Cs, 2 Ds, 2 Es
10. 1 J, 1 Q, 2 Ks
11. 1 red ball, 3 blue balls, 3 green balls or
    3 red balls, 2 blue balls, 2 green balls or
    5 red balls, 1 blue ball, 1 green ball
12. one 1, one 2, three 3s, one 4 ; or
    one 1, two 2s, two 3s, one 4 ; or
    one 1, three 2s, one 3, one 4 ; or
    two 1s, one 2, one 3, two 4s
13. A, B, C
14.

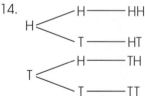

15a. C   b. C
   c. C   d. A
   e. C

1 Operations with Whole Numbers

Try It
3012 ; 5775

1. 169	2. 262
3. 3514	4. 3282
5. 6559	6. 5581
7. 311	8. 4232
9. 4133	10. 4349
11. 3725	12. 1952
13. 2731	14. 5400
15. 461	16. 3729
17. 1501	18. 5940
19. 85	20. 612
21. 73	22. 65
23. 676	24. 291
25. 731	26. 684
27. 92	28. 73
29. 1105	30. 1862
31. 1458	32. 33
33. 952	34. 55
35. 99	36. 47
37. 852	38. 135
39. 76	40. 1232

41. 178 ; 4 ; 178 ; 5 ; 4 ; 894
42. 17R1 ; 17 x 7 + 1 = 120
43. 368R1 ; 368 x 2 + 1 = 737
44. 41R3 ; 41 x 9 + 3 = 372
45. 24R5 ; 24 x 6 + 5 = 149

46. ✔	47. ✔
48. 34	49. ✔
50. 20	51. ✔
52. ✔	53. ✔
54. 1	55. ✔
56. 20	57. 90
58. 50	59. 70 000
60. ✔	61. 700
62. 117R1	63. 96R2
64. 121R7	65. 102R8
66. 72R3	67. 85R4

If you can decode my message, well done!

68. 381	69. 235
70. 1218	71. 3344
72. 120	73. 210
74. 4854	75. 6
76. 187	77. 29
78. 72	

2	3	5	1	8	7
5	1	2	1	8	4
7	2	3	1	1	8
2	9	8	2	2	5
0	7	1	0	1	4
3	3	4	4	0	6

13

2 Adding and Subtracting Decimals

Try It
1.46 ; 4.57

1. 1.4 ; 18.9
2. = 2.5 – 0.5
   = 2
3. = 2 + 4.99
   = 6.99
4. = 11.5 + 2.52
   = 14.02
5. = 11 – 0.56
   = 10.44
6. = 2.25 – 0.75
   = 1.5

7a. 0 ; 7.93 ; 15.95 ; 24.53 ; 58.05 ; 45.48 ; 24.45

10.14	15.95	4.99	16.73
7.93	58.05	45.48	24.53
0.86	20.11	1.07	24.45
9.7	4.99	0	30.51

b. 4.69 ; 2.8 ; 5.01 ; 2.93 ; 4.8 ; 8.8 ; 1.8

9.8	1.8	15.19	8.8
15.6	4.69	48.56	2.8
3.09	2.93	5.01	9.19
4.8	10.8	35.2	3.8

Jane

8. 10.72
   Sum:
   ```
     7.10
   + 3.62
   ------
    10.72
   ```
   Estimate:
   ```
     7
   + 4
   ---
    11
   ```

9. 5.87
   Sum:
   ```
     0.09
   + 5.78
   ------
     5.87
   ```
   Estimate:
   ```
     0
   + 6
   ---
     6
   ```

10. 10.25

Sum:	Estimate:
7.30	7
+ 2.95	+ 3
10.25	10

11. 20.63

Sum:	Estimate:
17.55	18
+ 3.08	+ 3
20.63	21

12. 54.97

Sum:	Estimate:
28.07	28
+ 26.90	+ 27
54.97	55

13.
Difference:	Estimate:
13.00	13
− 8.02	− 8
4.98	5

14.
Difference:	Estimate:
15.25	15
− 6.75	− 7
8.50	8

15.
Difference:	Estimate:
29.63	30
− 24.96	− 25
4.67	5

16.
Difference:	Estimate:
45.92	46
− 26.31	− 26
19.61	20

17. = 18.25 − 8.25 + 6.99
= 10 + 6.99
= 16.99

18. = 30.99 + 2.01 − 4.5
= 33 − 4.5
= 28.5

19. = 9.45 + 3.55 − 2.33
= 13 − 2.33
= 10.67

20. = 16.12 − 8.12 + 6.8
= 8 + 6.8
= 14.8

21. = 17.46 − 5.46 − 8.99
= 12 − 8.99
= 3.01

22. = 2.05 + 7.95 + 9.46
= 10 + 9.46
= 19.46

23. = 10.99 + 3.01 − 2.35
= 14 − 2.35
= 11.65

24. = 28.31 − 5.31 − 1.49
= 23 − 1.49
= 21.51

25. = 8.95 + 11.05 + 4.5 − 2.34
= 20 + 4.5 − 2.34
= 24.5 − 2.34
= 22.16

26. = 39.65 + 21.35 + 4.8 − 19.38
= 61 + 4.8 − 19.38
= 65.8 − 19.38
= 46.42

3　Multiplying and Dividing Decimals

Try It
49 ; 0.36

1. 73.4
2. 0.923
3. 0.1234
4. 24.2
5. 0.369
6. 120
7. 15
8. 8.08
9. 3.42
10. 34 290
11. 125
12. 2
13. 400
14. 1180
15. 6
16. 1.25
17. 2.2
18. 635
19. 0.5
20. 3.9
21. x
22. x
23. ÷
24. ÷
25. ÷
26. x
27. x
28. x

29. Tim:
1: ✔　　　　2: ✔
3: 100 ; 1000　　4: 100 ; 10
5: ✔　　　　6: 1000 ; 10
Kim:
1: ✔　　　　2: ✔
3: ✔　　　　4: ✔
5: 100 ; 1000　　6: 10 ; 100
Kim

30. 3 ; 0.3

31. = 450 ÷ 10
= 45

32. = 280 ÷ 10
= 28

33. = 4.75 x 1000
= 4750

34. = 2.85 x 100
= 285

35. = 60 300 ÷ 100
= 603

36. = 10.95 x 100
= 1095

37. = 1475 ÷ 10
= 147.5

38. = 32 400 ÷ 1000
= 32.4

39. = 19.84 x 100
= 1984

40. = 249 ÷ 1000
    = 0.249
42. 2.49
44. 0.507
46. 4.5
48. 16.8 x 10
50. 460 ÷ 100
52. smaller

41. 60

43. 0.928
45. 2
47. 580 ÷ 1000
49. 205 ÷ 1000
51. 1000 ; right
53. Dividing ; 1

53. 3
55. $3\frac{1}{3}$
57. $3\frac{1}{5}$
59. $\cancel{\frac{5}{2}}$; $\boxed{1\frac{1}{2}}$
61. $2\cancel{\frac{7}{3}}$; $\boxed{3\frac{1}{3}}$

54. ✔
56. ✔
58. $1\frac{4}{5}$
60. $\cancel{\frac{23}{10}}$; $\boxed{2\frac{3}{5}}$

4 Equivalent Fractions

Try It
6 ; 10

1. 2 ; 8
3. 5 ; 6
5. 20 ; $\frac{5}{15}$; $\frac{30}{45}$
7. 12 ; $\frac{8}{20}$; $\frac{32}{80}$
9. 8 ; 8
11. 7 ; 7
13. 9 ; 9
15. 5 ; 2
17. 55 ; 4
19. 4 ; 18

2. 9 ; 9
4. 4 ; 10
6. 4 ; $\frac{2}{10}$; $\frac{6}{8}$
8. 10 ; 10
10. 5 ; 5
12. 7 ; 7
14. 3 ; 12
16. 2 ; 4
18. 20 ; 6

20-25. (Suggested answers)
20. $\frac{2}{16}$; $\frac{3}{24}$; $\frac{4}{32}$
22. $\frac{1}{4}$; $\frac{2}{8}$; $\frac{4}{16}$
24. $\frac{10}{12}$; $\frac{15}{18}$; $\frac{20}{24}$
26. 2
28. 4
30. 3
32. $\frac{2}{3}$
34. $\frac{4}{5}$
36. $\frac{1}{2}$
38. $\frac{3}{7}$
40. $\frac{2}{3}$
42. E ; F ; B ;
    C ; D ; A
43. $3\frac{1}{3}$
45. ✔
47. $4\frac{1}{3}$
49. $2\frac{1}{2}$
51. $1\frac{1}{5}$

21. $\frac{4}{6}$; $\frac{6}{9}$; $\frac{8}{12}$
23. $\frac{10}{14}$; $\frac{15}{21}$; $\frac{20}{28}$
25. $\frac{7}{10}$; $\frac{21}{30}$; $\frac{28}{40}$
27. 2
29. 3
31. 1
33. $\frac{3}{8}$
35. $\frac{5}{6}$
37. $\frac{2}{11}$
39. $\frac{1}{4}$
41. $\frac{4}{7}$

44. $1\frac{1}{2}$
46. $2\frac{2}{7}$
48. $\frac{3}{5}$
50. $3\frac{1}{3}$
52. ✔

5 Ordering Fractions

Try It
$\frac{9}{12}$; $\frac{10}{12}$; <

1a. <
 c. =
 e. >
 g. >
2a. >
 c. >
 e. <
 g. <
3a. >
 c. =
 e. <
 g. >

b. <
d. >
f. >

b. >
d. <
f. =

b. <
d. <
f. <

4. $\frac{1}{5}$; $\frac{2}{5}$; $\frac{4}{5}$; $\frac{3}{5}$
   $\frac{6}{15}$; $\frac{12}{20}$; $\frac{8}{10}$
5. $\frac{1}{3}$; $\frac{1}{6}$; $\frac{1}{2}$; $\frac{5}{6}$
   $\frac{2}{12} < \frac{6}{18} < \frac{12}{24} < \frac{25}{30}$
6. $\frac{5}{8}$; $\frac{1}{2}$; $\frac{7}{8}$; $\frac{3}{4}$
   $\frac{15}{30} < \frac{10}{16} < \frac{15}{20} < \frac{21}{24}$
7. $\frac{7}{10}$; $\frac{4}{5}$; $\frac{1}{2}$; $\frac{3}{5}$
   $\frac{11}{22} < \frac{27}{45} < \frac{21}{30} < \frac{20}{25}$
8. $\frac{9}{5}$; $2\frac{1}{5}$; $\frac{13}{5}$ 9. $\frac{6}{4}$; $1\frac{3}{4}$; $\frac{10}{4}$
10. $\frac{10}{7}$; $1\frac{4}{7}$; $\frac{13}{7}$ 11. $\frac{4}{3}$; $1\frac{2}{3}$; $\frac{7}{3}$
12. $3\frac{4}{6}$; $\frac{20}{6}$; $3\frac{1}{6}$; $\frac{17}{6}$
13. $2\frac{7}{8}$; $\frac{21}{8}$; $2\frac{3}{8}$; $\frac{18}{8}$
14. $\frac{1}{3} < \frac{2}{3} < 1\frac{1}{3} < \frac{5}{3}$
15. $\frac{6}{7} < 1\frac{1}{7} < \frac{9}{7} < 1\frac{3}{7}$
16. $\frac{7}{8} < \frac{9}{8} < \frac{10}{8} < 1\frac{3}{8} < 1\frac{5}{8}$

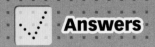

Answers

17. $\frac{5}{3} < \frac{7}{3} < 2\frac{2}{3} < \frac{9}{3} < \frac{15}{3}$

18. $1\frac{3}{4} < 2\frac{1}{4} < \frac{11}{4} < \frac{16}{4} < \frac{17}{4}$

19a. red: $\frac{3}{7}$; blue: $1\frac{2}{7}$

b. red: $\frac{7}{9}$; blue: $2\frac{1}{9}$

c. red: $1\frac{5}{6}$; blue: $\frac{20}{6}$

d. red: $1\frac{1}{8}$; blue: $2\frac{1}{8}$

20-25. (Suggested answers)

20a. $\frac{3}{7}$ b. $\frac{3}{5}$

21a. $\frac{10}{9}$ b. $\frac{8}{6}$

22a. $2\frac{2}{3}$ b. $1\frac{7}{9}$

23. ; $1\frac{3}{8}$

24. 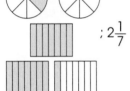 ; $2\frac{1}{7}$

25.  ; $2\frac{1}{6}$

6 Fractions and Decimals

Try It

$\frac{3}{10}$; $\frac{17}{20}$

1. $\frac{3}{10}$ 2. $\frac{9}{10}$

3. $\frac{31}{100}$ 4. $\frac{9}{100}$

5. $\frac{7}{10}$ 6. $\frac{1}{10}$

7. $\frac{9}{20}$ 8. $\frac{22}{25}$

9. $\frac{1}{100}$ 10. $\frac{1}{4}$

11. $\frac{11}{100}$ 12. $\frac{1}{2}$

13. $\frac{1}{5}$ 14. $\frac{53}{100}$

15. $\frac{1}{20}$ 16. $\frac{2}{25}$

17. $\frac{4}{25}$ 18. $\frac{2}{5}$

19. $\frac{13}{20}$ 20. $\frac{47}{50}$

21. 0.7 22. 0.03

23. 0.49 24. 0.09
25. 0.73 26. 0.87
27. 0.99 28. 0.003
29. 0.013 30. 0.467
31. 0.087 32. 0.159

33. $\frac{5}{10}$; 0.5 34. $\frac{2}{10}$; 0.2

35. $\frac{75}{100}$; 0.75 36. $\frac{6}{10}$; 0.6

37. $\frac{125}{1000}$; 0.125 38. $\frac{625}{1000}$; 0.625

39. $\frac{375}{1000}$; 0.375 40. $\frac{8}{10}$; 0.8

41. $\frac{28}{100}$; 0.28 42. $\frac{58}{100}$; 0.58

43. $\frac{998}{1000}$; 0.998 44. $\frac{72}{1000}$; 0.072

45. $\frac{572}{1000}$; 0.572

46a. $\frac{13}{20}$ b. $\frac{3}{4}$

c. $\frac{9}{25}$ d. $1\frac{1}{5}$

e. $1\frac{1}{2}$ f. $2\frac{3}{20}$

g. $1\frac{1}{100}$ h. $2\frac{3}{4}$

47a. 0.25 b. 0.85 c. 0.76
d. 1.125 e. 1.4 f. 2.8
g. 3.5 h. 2.25

48. 0.25 ; 25 49. 0.40 ; 40
50. 0.75 ; 75 51. 0.60 ; 60
52. 0.70 ; 70 53. 0.90 ; 90
54. 0.65 55. 0.9

56. $1\frac{2}{5}$ 57. $\frac{2}{3}$

58. 4.26 59. 0.57
60. 3.69 61. 8.38

62. $6\frac{3}{8}$ 63. $1.54 ; 1\frac{7}{8} ; 1\frac{8}{9}$

64. $2\frac{4}{7} < 2\frac{3}{5} < 2.68$ 65. $5\frac{4}{5} < 5.83 < 5\frac{9}{10}$

66a. 0.125 ; 0.25 ; 0.75 ; 0.375 ; 0.875 ; 0.2

b. $\frac{1}{8} ; \frac{1}{5} ; \frac{1}{4} ; \frac{3}{8} ; \frac{3}{4} ; \frac{7}{8}$

67a. $\frac{3}{5} ; \frac{17}{20} ; \frac{27}{50} ; \frac{9}{25} ; \frac{3}{4} ; 1\frac{1}{2}$

b. $1\frac{1}{2} ; \frac{17}{20} ; \frac{3}{4} ; \frac{3}{5} ; \frac{27}{50} ; \frac{9}{25}$

7 Money

Try It

Bill/Coin	No.	Subtotal
$10	3	$30
$5	3	$15
$1	6	$6
	Total:	$51

1.

Bill/Coin	No.	Subtotal
$20	2	$40
$2	5	$10
$0.10	6	$0.60
$0.05	3	$0.15
	Total:	$50.75

2.

Bill/Coin	No.	Subtotal
$10	3	$30
$5	3	$15
$1	5	$5
$0.25	3	$0.75
	Total:	$50.75

3-5. (Individual drawings for another way)

3.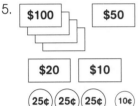

4.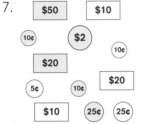

5.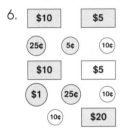

6.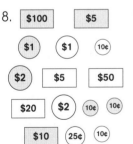

7.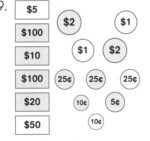

8.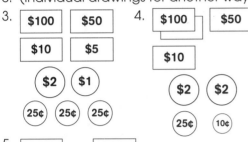

9.

10. $205 ; B
11. $170.65 ; B
12. $267.50 ; C

8 Perimeter and Area

Try It
16 ; 15

1. 12 cm
2. 27 m
3. 30 km
4. 20 km
5. 32 cm
6. 18 m
7. 39 mm

8a. A: 12 cm ; 9 cm²   B: 16 cm ; 11 cm²
    C: 24 cm ; 13 cm²   D: 16 cm ; 12 cm²
    E: 22 cm ; 15 cm²   F: 22 cm ; 16 cm²

b. Shape A ; Shape C ; Shape A ; Shape F

9. Shape A:
Perimeter: 7 x 4 = 28 (cm)
Area: 7 x 7 = 49 (cm²)
Shape B:
Perimeter: 6 x 2 + 2 x 2 = 16 (cm)
Area: 6 x 2 = 12 (cm²)
Shape C:
Perimeter: 8 x 2 + 1 x 2 = 18 (cm)
Area: 8 x 1 = 8 (cm²)
Shape D:
Perimeter: 8 x 2 + 4 x 2 = 24 (cm)
Area: 8 x 4 = 32 (cm²)

10. Shape A   11. Shape B
12. Shape D

13.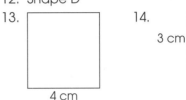

4 cm
P: 16 cm
A: 16 cm²

14.
3 cm
5 cm
P: 16 cm
A: 15 cm²

15.

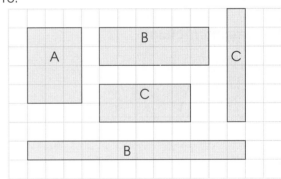

9 Mass

Try It
g ; kg

1.

2a. 2000   b. 5000
 c. 11 000   d. 7
 e. 3   f. 4

3a. 4000   b. 2000
 c. 10 000   d. 3
 e. 8   f. 5

4a. 3000   b. 6000
 c. 9000   d. 4
 e. 2   f. 17

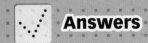
5. 185 000 ; 0.185 ; 0.000185
6. 500 000 000 ; 500 000 ; 500
7. 125 000 000 ; 125 000 ; 0.125
8. B   9. B
10. A   11. B
12. A   13. A
14. B, D, C, A   15. D, B, A, C
16. 0.62 kg = 620 g
    Sum: 620 + 430 = 1050 (g)
    Difference: 620 – 430 = 190 (g)
17. 15 000 mg = 15 g
    Sum: 80 + 15 = 95 (g)
    Difference: 80 – 15 = 65 (g)
18. 1.3 t = 1300 kg
    Sum: 1300 + 250 = 1550 (kg)
    Difference: 1300 – 250 = 1050 (kg)
19. 87 g = 87 000 mg
    Sum: 7800 + 87 000 = 94 800 (mg)
    Difference: 87 000 – 7800 = 79 200 (mg)
20. 2.2 kg = 2200 g
    Sum: 2200 + 440 = 2640 (g)
    Difference: 2200 – 440 = 1760 (g)

10 Transformations

Try It

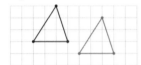

1.

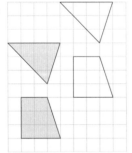

2.

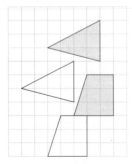

3.

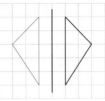

4.

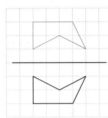

5.

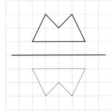

6.

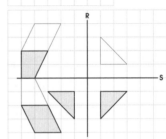

7.   8.

9.   10.

       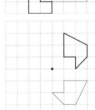

11.

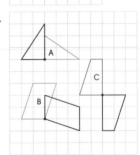

The second rotated image is the same as the original.

12.

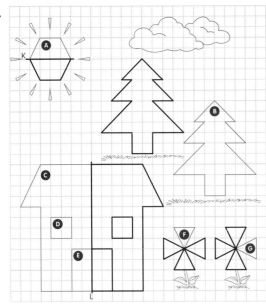

11 Patterning

Try It
8 ; 6 ; 4 ; 2

1. 9 ; 7 ; 5 ; 3 ; 1

2. 1, 2, 4, 8, 16

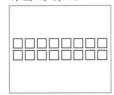

3. 5, 4, 3, 2, 1

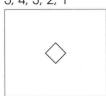

4. D ; A ; B ; C

5a. Pattern B   b. Pattern A

c. Pattern C   d. Pattern D

6. yes   7. Pattern B

8.

a. No. of Identical Triangles: 1 ; 2 ; 3 ; 4
No. of Sticks: 3 ; 5 ; 7 ; 9

b. Start at 1. Add 1 each time.
Start at 3. Add 2 each time.

c. 5 ; 7   d. 11 ; 13

e. Frame 8 ; Frame 7

9.

a. 15 ; 14 ; 7 ; 6 ; 3

b. Start at 15. Subtract 1. Then divide by 2.

c. 2 dots ; 1 dot

10.

a. 22 ; 11 ; 14 ; 7 ; 10

b. Start at 22. Divide by 2. Then add 3.

c. 5 blocks ; 4 blocks

12 Equations

Try It
A

1. C   2. C

3. A   4. B

5. B   6. A

7. $n \div 3 = 4$ 8. $r + 4 = 15$

9. $k \times 2 = 20$ 10. $f - 6 = 12$

11. $17 + j = 26$
$j = 9$
9

12. $p - 11 = 28$
$p = 39$
39

13. $d \times 2 = 20$
$d = 10$
10

14. $24 \div g = 4$
$g = 6$
6

15. $8 \times y = 64$
$y = 8$
8

16. $m \div 2 = 50$
$m = 100$
100

17. B ; 9   18. A ; 15

19. A ; 8   20. A ; 8

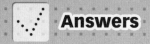

21. $14 + c = 33$
$c = 19$
19

22. $60 - p = 10$
$p = 50$
50

23. $45 \div b = 9$
$b = 5$
5

24. $b \times 3 = 24$
$b = 8$
8

25. $27 - d = 18$
$d = 9$
9

13 Graphs

Try It
B

1a. B   b. A   c. B
2a. A   b. A   c. B
3a. hockey   b. tennis
c. 4 children   d. 19 children
e. 6 children   f. 6 children
g. 3 sports   h. 30 children
i. 45 children
4a. car   b. motorcycle
c. 20 employees   d. 40 employees
e. 65 employees   f. 25 employees
g. 80 employees   h. truck
i.

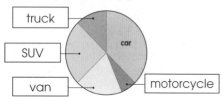

Types of Vehicles Employees Drive

5. A
a. 65 thousand people
b. 130 thousand people
c. 2005
d. 8 thousand people
e. 60 thousand people
f. between 1990 and 1995
g. between 2000 and 2005

14 Probability

Try It
$\frac{1}{6}$; $\frac{1}{3}$

1a. $\frac{1}{6}$ b. $\frac{1}{6}$ c. $\frac{1}{6}$
d. 0   e. $\frac{1}{2}$
2a. $\frac{1}{8}$ b. $\frac{1}{2}$ c. 0
d. $\frac{1}{4}$ e. $\frac{1}{4}$

3a. $\frac{1}{12}$ b. $\frac{1}{4}$ c. $\frac{1}{3}$
d. $\frac{1}{12}$ e. $\frac{1}{3}$ f. $\frac{3}{4}$
g. $\frac{1}{4}$ h. $\frac{1}{12}$ i. 0
j. $\frac{1}{4}$

4a. B   b. $\frac{1}{12}$; $\frac{1}{12}$
$\frac{1}{2}$; 1
$\frac{1}{6}$; $\frac{1}{4}$

5.

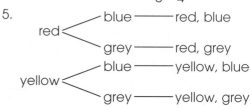

a. 4   b. $\frac{1}{4}$; $\frac{1}{2}$; 0

6.

+	1	2	3	4	5	6
1	2	3	4	5	6	7
2	3	4	5	6	7	8
3	4	5	6	7	8	9
4	5	6	7	8	9	10
5	6	7	8	9	10	11
6	7	8	9	10	11	12

a. 11
b. $\frac{1}{36}$; $\frac{1}{12}$; $\frac{1}{12}$; $\frac{1}{2}$; $\frac{1}{2}$; $\frac{7}{12}$; $\frac{1}{6}$

7.

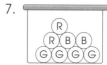

a. $\frac{1}{4}$ b. $\frac{1}{2}$ c. 0

8.

a. $\frac{2}{7}$ b. $\frac{2}{7}$ c. $\frac{4}{7}$

9.

a. $\frac{3}{8}$ b. $\frac{1}{8}$ c. $\frac{1}{8}$
d. $\frac{5}{8}$ e. $\frac{7}{8}$ f. $\frac{1}{2}$

1 Operations with Whole Numbers (1)

Try It
55 ; 12 ; 660
2419 ; 660 ; 3079
3079

1. 11¢ x 34 = 374¢
   The total value is 374¢.
2. 135¢ ÷ 9 = 15¢
   Each nickel is worth 15¢.
3. 14¢ x 31 = 434¢
   The total value is 434¢.
4. Valuable quarters: 116¢ x 5 = 580¢
   Other quarters: 76¢ x 14 = 1064¢
   Total: 580¢ + 1064¢ = 1644¢
   The total value is 1644¢.
5a. 942 ÷ 6 = 157
   There are 157 g of raisins in each bag.
   b. 896 ÷ 8 = 112
   There are 112 g of peanuts in each pile.
   c. 15 x 63 = 945
   Each bag of figs weighs 945 g.
   d. 486 ÷ 6 = 81
   Each person, including Allan, gets 81 cookies.
   e. Bags of 5: 486 ÷ 5 = 97R1
   Bags of 7: 486 ÷ 7 = 69R3
   Dividing the cookies into bags of 7 will result in more cookies left over.
   f. 896 ÷ 25 = 35R21
   He needs 36 bags.
   g. No. of apricots: 32 x 15 = 480
   Apricots in each bag: 480 ÷ 5 = 96
   There will be 96 apricots in each bag.
6a. 648 ÷ 9 = 72
   He needs 72 boxes.
   b. $11 x 72 = $792
   The boxes will cost $792 in all.
7a. 108 ÷ 9 = 12
   There are 12 rows.
   b. 15 x 12 = 180
   The pansies need 180 g of fertilizer.
8. No. of marbles in a bag: 448 ÷ 8 = 56
   Weight of each bag: 12 x 56 = 672
   The total weight is 672 g.
9. No. of beans: 56 x 11 = 616
   No. of beans in each bag: 616 ÷ 8 = 77
   There will be 77 beans in each bag.

10. 25 ÷ 5 x 365 = 1825
    He jogs for 1825 min.
11. 24 x 12 ÷ 9 = 32
    There will be 32 blocks in each tower.
12. $11 x 738 ÷ 6 = $1353
    The light bulbs cost $1353 altogether.
13. $840 ÷ $15 ÷ 4 = 14
    She worked 14 shifts.
14. $960 ÷ $4 ÷ 6 = 40
    There were 40 students on each bus.

2 Operations with Whole Numbers (2)

Try It
2 x 3 x 7 = 42
42

1a. 752 + 598 + 208 = 1558
   There are 1558 planks in all.
   b. Total no. of planks: 752 + 208 = 960
   No. of bundles: 960 ÷ 8 = 120
   There are 120 bundles.
   c. 2 x 112 x 8 = 1792
   1792 m of lumber is sold in all.
   d. No. of planks left: 598 – 269 = 329
   Total length: 2 x 329 = 658
   658 m of oak is left.
2a. No. of students: 12 + 11 = 23
   No. of pencils: 3 x 23 = 69
   69 pencils were given out.
   b. Total no. of pencils: 69 + 7 = 76
   No. of packs: 76 ÷ 4 = 19
   There were 19 packs of pencils.
3a. 1938 – 1805 = 133
   He threw 133 cm farther.
   b. Mario and Jimmy: 1236 + 1938 = 3174
   Sandy and Dolores: 1805 + 1647 = 3452
   Sandy and Dolores had a greater total distance.
   c. Danny: 1475 + 1475 = 2950
   Difference: 3452 – 2950 = 502
   The winning team threw 502 cm farther.
4a. Panes of glass in doors: 8 x 11 = 88
   Panes of glass in windows: 2 x 32 = 64
   Total: 88 + 64 = 152
   There are 152 panes of glass in all.
   b. $12 x 2 x 32 = $768
   It costs $768.
   c. $15 ÷ 2 x 8 x 11 = $660
   It costs $660.
   d. $768 + $660 – $250 = $1178
   It costs $1178.

5. One roll of ribbon:
   108 ÷ 9 = 12 (m) = 1200 (cm)
   No. of strips: 1200 ÷ 20 = 60
   There are 60 strips.

6. Total amount of juice: 510 + 378 = 888
   Amount in each cup: 888 ÷ 4 = 222
   There will be 222 mL of fruit punch in each cup.

7. 2 jackets: $75 x 2 = $150
   3 pairs of jeans: $34 x 3 = $102
   Total: $150 + $102 = $252
   He paid $252.

8. Cost of CDs: $15 + $18 = $33
   Mario's money: $20 + $10 + $5 = $35
   Yes, he can afford the two CDs.

9. Walking to library: 20 + 20 = 40
   Running to library: 14 + 14 = 28
   Time saved: (40 − 28) x 7 = 84
   She can save 84 min in a week.

10. No. of times doubled: 21 ÷ 7 = 3
    Value: $55 x 2 x 2 x 2 = $440
    It will be worth $440.

11. Total no. of cards: 382 + 382 + 148 = 912
    No. of cards in each album: 912 ÷ 3 = 304
    There will be 304 cards in each album.

3 Decimals (1)

Try It
160.48 ; 160.48 ; 160.48

1. 0.75 + 1.28 = 2.03
   There is 2.03 L of juice.

2. 5 − 2.68 = 2.32
   2.32 kg of peanuts are left.

3. $8.60 ÷ 10 = $0.86
   Each juice box cost $0.86.

4. $35.50 x 10 = $355
   It costs $355.

5. $39.55 − $28.62 = $10.93
   He has $10.93 left.

6. 1.83 − 0.27 = 1.56
   The second tree is 1.56 m tall.

7. 215.62 + 360.82 = 576.44
   They weigh 576.44 g altogether.

8. 2.31 − 1.92 = 0.39
   She was 0.39 h faster.

9. 120 ÷ 1000 = 0.12
   The weight of each bar of soap is 0.12 kg.

10. 9.46 x 100 = 946
    100 packets hold 946 mL of ketchup.

11a. $11.29 − $8.55 = $2.74
     She spent $2.74 more.
  b. $8.55 + $11.29 = $19.84
     They spent $19.84 altogether.

12a. $19.99 + $25.45 = $45.44
     The items cost $45.44 altogether.
  b. Yes, he has enough.
     $50 − $45.44 = $4.56
     He will have $4.56 left.

13a. 5.9 − 1.38 = 4.52
     They have to walk 4.52 km farther.
  b. 5.9 + 1.25 = 7.15
     Black Bird Trail is 7.15 km long.

14a. $2.49 x 10 = $24.90
     10 small boxes of napkins cost $24.90.
  b. $24.90 − $20.58 = $4.32
     The price difference is $4.32.

15. Cost of 1 pencil: $35 ÷ 100 = $0.35
    Total cost: $0.35 + $0.35 + $0.59 = $1.29
    The total cost is $1.29.

16a. 7.7 x 10 = 77
     There is 77 g of sugar.
  b. 5.5 ÷ 10 = 0.55
     There is 0.55 mg of salt.
  c. 7.7 ÷ 10 x 1000 = 770
     There is 770 g of sugar.

4 Decimals (2)

Try It
$5.70
$5.70 ; $4.30
$4.30

1. $12.37 + $14.62 = $26.99
   The total cost is $26.99.

2. Amount saved for 1 USB: $16 − $14.62 = $1.38
   Amount saved for 10 USBs: $1.38 x 10 = $13.80
   He saved $13.80.

3. $150 − $67.99 − $67.99 = $14.02
   Her change was $14.02.

4. $12.37 + $1.59 + $67.99 = $81.95
   The total price was $81.95.

5a. $9.50 + $15.09 = $24.59
    A tie and a belt cost $24.59 altogether.
  b. $18.20 + $21.35 = $39.55
     2 blouses and a dress cost $39.55 in all.
  c. $14.85 + $14.85 = $29.70
     20 pairs of socks cost $29.70.
  d. $14.85 ÷ 10 x 100 = $148.50
     100 pairs of socks cost $148.50.

e. Cost of 10 ties: $9.50 x 10 = $95
   After coupon: $95 – $20 = $75
   He needs to pay $75.

6a. $8.50 x 1000 = $8500
    The theatre will make $8500.

 b. $5.32 x 100 = $532
    The theatre will make $532.

 c. 1 gift certificate: $8.50 + $5.32 = $13.82
    10 gift certificates: $13.82 x 10 = $138.20
    10 gift certificates cost $138.20.

 d. 1 gift certificate: $8.50 + $5.32 – $2.86 = $10.96
    100 gift certificates: $10.96 x 100 = $1096
    100 gift certificates cost $1096.

7a. $24.99 + $24.99 + 24.99 = $74.97
    It costs $74.97.

 b. $74.97 + $24.99 – $89.38 = $10.58
    They will save $10.58.

8a. 0.3 km = 0.3 x 1000 m = 300 m
    Rachel lives closest to the school. She lives
    300 m away.

 b. 1620 m = 1620 ÷ 1000 km = 1.62 km
    The distance is 1.62 km.

 c. 1.57 + 0.89 = 2.46
    It is 2.46 km away.

 d. Passing by Virginia's house: 2.46 km
    Passing by Sandra's house:
    0.93 + 1.35 = 2.28
    Passing by Paul's and Rachel's houses:
    1.32 + 2.82 + 0.3 = 4.44
    Passing by Sandra's house is the shortest
    distance.
    2.28 km = 2.28 x 1000 m = 2280 m
    The shortest distance is 2280 m.

5   Fractions

Try It
8 ; 9
Kari

1.

Tim ate less.

2.   served   ate
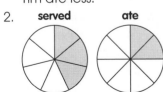
She served more cake than she ate.

3.   **red**   **blue**
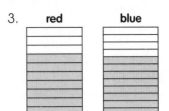
He built more of the red train.

4. **Dan**
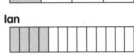

Ian

Ian has more cards.

5. Apple: $\frac{3}{4}$

   Pear: $\frac{1}{4}$

   Banana: $\frac{2}{4} = \frac{1}{2}$

   Each child gets $\frac{3}{4}$ of an apple, $\frac{1}{4}$ of a pear,
   and $\frac{1}{2}$ of a banana.

6a. $\frac{9}{6} = 1\frac{1}{2}$
    Each child will get $1\frac{1}{2}$ chocolate bars.

 b. $\frac{9}{4} = 2\frac{1}{4}$
    Each child will get $2\frac{1}{4}$ chocolate bars.

7. Peter: $6\frac{1}{2} = 6\frac{4}{8}$ Joe: $6\frac{3}{8}$
   Peter's hat size is larger.

8. Nina: $5\frac{3}{5} = 5\frac{12}{20}$ Jenna: $5\frac{3}{4} = 5\frac{15}{20}$
   Jenna ran farther.

9. Bob: $3\frac{1}{6} = 3\frac{5}{30}$ Jim: $3\frac{3}{10} = 3\frac{9}{30}$
   Bob's eatery used fewer napkins.

10. $\frac{1}{2}$ hour = 30 minutes
    Mary read it faster.

11a. $\frac{2}{5}$ of 30 is 12.
     There are 12 girls in the class.

 b. $\frac{1}{6}$ of 30 is 5.
    5 students were not in class on Friday.

 c. $\frac{9}{30} = \frac{3}{10}$
    $\frac{3}{10}$ of the students have sandwiches for
    lunch.

12. 26 – 5 = 21
    Consonants make up $\frac{21}{26}$ of the alphabet.

13. $\frac{18}{30} = \frac{3}{5}$
    He worked $\frac{3}{5}$ of the month.

14. This statement is false.

$\frac{15}{4} = 3\frac{3}{4}$

$\frac{13}{3} = 4\frac{1}{3}$ ← larger

Numerators and denominators cannot be compared separately.

15a. $\frac{3}{12} = \frac{1}{4}$

Each child gets $\frac{1}{4}$ of a pizza.

b. $\frac{1}{3}$ of 12 is 4.

There are 4 girls at the party.

c. 16 – 12 = 4

$\frac{4}{16} = \frac{1}{4}$

$\frac{1}{4}$ of the cake is left over.

16a. $\frac{1}{2}$ h = 30 min

$\frac{3}{5}$ h = 36 min

$\frac{3}{4}$ h = 45 min

Having snacks takes the most time.

b. Playing in the backyard takes the least time.

17. Jon: $\frac{9}{12} = \frac{27}{36}$ Ali: $\frac{14}{18} = \frac{28}{36}$

Ali coloured more of her spinner.

6   Operations with Money

Try It

$20 ; $20 ; $5.05 ; $5.05

1. $15.48 + $35.17 = $50.65

Her bill will be $50.65.

2a. $15.48 + $10.09 + $35.17 + $48.74 – $12.50

= $96.98

His bill was $96.98.

b. $100 – $96.98 = $3.02

He got $3.02 back.

3. $15.48 + $9.76 = $25.24

He raked leaves and washed her car.

4. She earned $570.75 in Week 1, $462.20 in Week 2, $415.40 in Week 3, and $520.20 in Week 4.

5. $570.75 + $462.20 = $1032.95

$1032.95 was earned in the first two weeks.

6. $520.20 – $415.40 = $104.80

$104.80 more was earned in Week 4 than Week 3.

7. $570.75 + $462.20 + $415.40 + $520.20

= $1968.55

$1968.55 was earned over the four weeks.

8. $1968.55 – $528.25 = $1440.30

She made $1440.30 in profit.

9. $66.40 ; $61.65

10. $42.35 + $52.15 = $94.50

They cost $94.50 together.

11. $61.65 – $30.80 – $19.99 = $10.86

She will have $10.86 left.

12. $66.40 – $25.45 – $25.45 = $15.50

He will have $15.50 left.

13. Total money: $66.40 + $61.65 = $128.05

Total cost:

$25.45 + $30.80 + $42.35 + $52.15 + $19.99

= $170.74

No, they do not have enough money.

14a. $1.19 x 10 – $10.80 = $1.10

She would save $1.10.

b. $25 – $10.80 – $10.80 = $3.40

Her change was $3.40.

15a. Total discount: $1.50 x 8 = $12

Actual cost: $82.97 – $12 = $70.97

Change: $100 – $70.97 = $29.03

Her change is $29.03.

b. Total discount: $1.80 x 12 = $21.60

Actual cost: $120.45 – $21.60 = $98.85

The actual cost is $98.85.

c. Cost before discount: $16.99 x 3 = $50.97

Total discount: $1.50 x 5 = $7.50

Actual cost: $50.97 – $7.50 = $43.47

Change: $50 – $43.47 = $6.53

He saves $7.50. His change is $6.53.

d. Total discount if bought separately:

$1.50 x 9 x 2 = $27

Total discount if bought together:

$1.80 x 18 = $32.40

She should buy the boots together because it will save more money.

7   Time

Try It

2:17 ; 2 ;17

1. 2 ; 16 ; 1 h 52 min ; 1 h 54 min ;

2 h 32 min ; 2 h 21 min ; 1 h 34 min

Tea, Please!:   Endless Planet:

2 ; 16 $\overset{9\ \ \ 67}{\cancel{10}{:}\cancel{07}}$

                                      – 8 : 1 5

                                   ‾‾‾‾‾‾‾‾‾

                                      1 : 5 2

The Doll Boss:
$$
\begin{array}{r}
^{11}\ \,^{90}\\
\cancel{12{:}30}\\
-\ 10{:}36\\
\hline
1{:}54
\end{array}
$$

Silent Screech:
$$
\begin{array}{r}
^{7}\ ^{60}\\
\cancel{8{:}00}\\
-\ 5{:}28\\
\hline
2{:}32
\end{array}
$$

Fire Prince:
$$
\begin{array}{r}
^{5}\ ^{68}\\
\cancel{6{:}08}\\
-\ 3{:}47\\
\hline
2{:}21
\end{array}
$$

Love Together:
$$
\begin{array}{r}
^{8}\ ^{89}\\
\cancel{9{:}29}\\
-\ 7{:}55\\
\hline
1{:}34
\end{array}
$$

2a.
$$
\begin{array}{r}
9{:}40\\
+\ 0{:}57\\
\hline
\cancel{9{:}97}\\
10\ \ 37
\end{array}
$$
They reached the park at 10:37 a.m.
$$
\begin{array}{r}
10{:}37\\
+\ 0{:}40\\
\hline
\cancel{10{:}77}\\
11\ \ 17
\end{array}
$$
They left the park at 11:17 a.m.
$$
\begin{array}{r}
11{:}17\\
+\ 0{:}32\\
\hline
11{:}49
\end{array}
$$
They reached the grocery store at 11:49 a.m.
$$
\begin{array}{r}
11{:}49\\
+\ 0{:}17\\
\hline
\cancel{11{:}66}\\
12\ \ 06
\end{array}
$$
They left the grocery store at 12:06 p.m.

b.
$$
\begin{array}{r}
12{:}42\\
-\ 12{:}06\\
\hline
0{:}36
\end{array}
$$
It took them 36 min.

c. 57 + 32 + 36 = 125
125 min = 2 h 5 min
They walked 2 h 5 min in total.

d. 40 − 17 = 23
They spent 23 min longer at the park than the grocery store.

e.
$$
\begin{array}{r}
12{:}42\\
-\ 9{:}40\\
\hline
3{:}02
\end{array}
$$
They were away from home for 3 h 2 min.

3. Breaking into 2 Parts: 30 min ; 1 h 40 min ; 2 h 10 min
24-hour Notation: 11:30 ; 13:40
$$
\begin{array}{r}
13{:}40\\
-\ 11{:}30\\
\hline
2{:}10
\end{array}
$$
2 h 10 min

4. From 10:58 a.m. to noon: 1 h 2 min
From noon to 1:07 p.m.: 1 h 7 min
1 h 2 min + 1 h 7 min = 2 h 9 min
10:58 a.m. → 10:58
1:07 p.m. → 13:07
$$
\begin{array}{r}
13{:}07\\
-\ 10{:}58\\
\hline
2{:}09
\end{array}
$$
2 h 9 min

5. From 9:12 a.m. to noon: 2 h 48 min
From noon to 2:02 p.m.: 2 h 2 min
2 h 48 min + 2 h 2 min = 4 h 50 min
9:12 a.m. → 09:12
2:02 p.m. → 14:02
$$
\begin{array}{r}
14{:}02\\
-\ 9{:}12\\
\hline
4{:}50
\end{array}
$$
4 h 50 min

6. From 11:21 p.m. to midnight: 39 min
From midnight to 2:13 a.m.: 2 h 13 min
39 min + 2 h 13 min = 2 h 52 min
11:21 p.m. → 23:21
midnight → 00:00/24:00
2:13 a.m. → 02:13
$$
\begin{array}{r}
24{:}00\\
-\ 23{:}21\\
\hline
0{:}39
\end{array}
\qquad
\begin{array}{r}
2{:}13\\
-\ 0{:}00\\
\hline
2{:}13
\end{array}
\qquad
\begin{array}{r}
0{:}39\\
+\ 2{:}13\\
\hline
2{:}52
\end{array}
$$
2 h 52 min

7. From 10:35 a.m. to noon: 1 h 25 min
From noon to 5:43 p.m.: 5 h 43 min
1 h 25 min + 5 h 43 min = 7 h 8 min
10:35 a.m. → 10:35
5:43 p.m. → 17:43
$$
\begin{array}{r}
17{:}43\\
-\ 10{:}35\\
\hline
7{:}08
\end{array}
$$
7 h 8 min

8a. 8:16 a.m. → 08:16
4:05 p.m. → 16:05
$$
\begin{array}{r}
16{:}05\\
-\ 08{:}16\\
\hline
7{:}49
\end{array}
$$
He worked on it for 7 h 49 min.

b.
$$
\begin{array}{r}
3{:}32\\
-\ 2{:}20\\
\hline
1{:}12
\end{array}
$$
He started his work at 1:12 p.m.

9a. $\begin{array}{r} 10{:}26 \\ 0{:}37 \\ +\ \ 0{:}16 \\ \hline \cancel{10{:}79} \\ {\scriptstyle 11\ \ \ 19} \end{array}$

He reached the theatre at 11:19 a.m.

b. Movie A:
$\begin{array}{r} 11{:}45 \\ +\ \ 1{:}43 \\ \hline \cancel{12{:}88} \\ {\scriptstyle 13\ \ \ 28} \end{array}$

Movie B:
$\begin{array}{r} 12{:}10 \\ +\ \ 1{:}16 \\ \hline 13{:}26 \end{array}$

Movie B finishes first.

10a. $\begin{array}{r} 1{:}48 \\ +\ \ 0{:}23 \\ \hline \cancel{X{:}\cancel{71}} \\ {\scriptstyle 2\ \ \ 11} \end{array}$

Yes, she will be on time.

b. $\begin{array}{r} 11{:}45 \\ +\ \ 1{:}35 \\ \hline \cancel{12{:}80} \\ {\scriptstyle 13\ \ \ 20} \end{array}$

The show ends at 1:20 p.m.

8 Perimeter and Area

Try It
Perimeter: 3 ; 2 ; 10
Area: 3 ; 2 ; 6
10 m ; 6 m²

1a. A: P: 2 x 5 + 2 x 3 = 16 (cm)
    A: 5 x 3 = 15 (cm²)
B: P: 4 x 4 = 16 (cm)
    A: 4 x 4 = 16 (cm²)
C: P: 2 x 6 + 2 x 2 = 16 (cm)
    A: 6 x 2 = 12 (cm²)
D: P: 2 x 5 + 2 x 4 = 18 (cm)
    A: 5 x 4 = 20 (cm²)

b. (4 x 4) x 4 = 64
The perimeter would be 64 cm.

c. 20 x 100 = 2000
The area is 2000 cm².

2a. Length: 20 + 3 + 3 = 26
Width: 12 + 3 + 3 = 18
The dimensions of the framed picture are 26 cm by 18 cm.

b. 2 x 26 + 2 x 18 = 88
The perimeter is 88 cm.

c. 26 x 18 = 468
The area is 468 cm².

3a. Old monitor: 2 x 30 + 2 x 20 = 100
New monitor: 2 x 60 + 2 x 40 = 200
200 ÷ 100 = 2
Yes, the perimeter of the new monitor also doubles that of the old monitor.

b. Old monitor: 30 x 20 = 600
New monitor: 60 x 40 = 2400
2400 ÷ 600 = 4
No, the area of the new monitor is 4 times that of the old monitor.

4. P: 2 x 29 + 2 x 21 = 100
A: 29 x 21 = 609
The perimeter is 100 cm and the area is 609 cm².

5a. • Bathroom:
    2 x 4 + 2 x 5 = 18
    The perimeter is 18 m.
• Living room:
    2 x 10 + 2 x 8 = 36
    The perimeter is 36 m.
• Dining room and kitchen combined:
    2 x 13 + 2 x 6 + 2 x 5 = 48
    The perimeter is 48 m.
• Hallway and living room combined:
    2 x 10 + 2 x 8 + 2 x 7 + 3 – 3 = 50
    The perimeter is 50 m.

b. • Closet:
    3 x 5 = 15
    The area is 15 m².
• Balcony:
    3 x 4 = 12
    The area is 12 m².
• Living room and kitchen:
    10 x 8 + 5 x 6 = 110
    The area is 110 m².
• Bedroom and closet:
    7 x 6 + 3 x 5 = 57
    The area is 57 m².

c. Length: 13 + 6 = 19
Width: 10 + 5 = 15
P: 2 x 19 + 2 x 15 = 68
A: 19 x 15 = 285
The perimeter is 68 m and the area is 285 m².

6. P: 2 x 5 + 2 x 2 = 14
A: 5 x 2 = 10
The perimeter is 14 m and the area is 10 m².

7. P: 4 x 60 = 240
   A: 60 x 60 = 3600
   The perimeter is 240 cm and the area is 3600 cm².
8. 120 ÷ 4 = 30
   Each side is 30 cm long.
9. 400 ÷ 25 = 16
   Its width is 16 m.
10. Length: (46 – 5 – 5) ÷ 2 = 18
    Area: 18 x 5 = 90
    Its area is 90 cm².
11a. Room A: 4 + 3 x 5 + (4 – 3) = 20
     Room B: 6 + 5 + (6 – 4) + 2 + 4 + (5 – 2) = 22
     Total: 20 + 22 = 42
     42 m of baseboard is needed.
  b. Room A: 4 x 3 + 3 x 3 = 21
     Room B: 6 x 5 – 4 x 2 = 22
     Room B needs more laminate.

9 Volume, Capacity, and Mass

Try It
50 ; 30 ; 35 ; 52 500
52 500 ; 52 500 ; 52.5
52 500 cm³ ; 52.5 L

1a. Old aquarium:

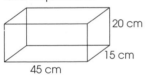

45 cm, 15 cm, 20 cm

New aquarium:

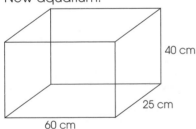

60 cm, 25 cm, 40 cm

  b. Old: 45 x 15 x 20 = 13 500 (cm³) = 13.5 (L)
     New: 60 x 25 x 40 = 60 000 (cm³) = 60 (L)
     The old aquarium's capacity is 13.5 L and the new aquarium's capacity is 60 L.
  c. Old: 13.5 L
     New: 60 ÷ 2 = 30
     30 – 13.5 = 16.5
     The new aquarium has more water by 16.5 L.

2a. 25 x 10 x 20 = 5000 (cm³)
    The volume of the pail is 5000 cm³.
  b. Tank: 160 000 mL = 160 L
     Pail: 5000 cm³ = 5000 mL = 5 L
     The tank holds 160 L and the pail holds 5 L.
  c. 8 x 5000 = 40 000
     40 000 cm³ of the tank will be empty.
     40 000 cm³ = 40 L
     160 – 40 = 120
     120 L of water will remain in the tank.
  d. 160 ÷ 2 ÷ 5 = 16
     16 pails of water must be removed.
  e. 160 000 ÷ 100 ÷ 25 = 64
     The minimum height needed is 64 cm.
  f. 75 000 ÷ 6 = 12 500
     The volume of each metal ball is 12 500 cm³.
3. C ; mL
4. V ; cm³
5. M ; kg
6. C : L
7. Weight gained: 100 g x 5 = 500 g = 0.5 kg
   Final weight: 3.2 + 0.5 = 3.7
   He weighed 3.7 kg after 5 weeks.
8. 1.4 t = 1400 kg
   1400 ÷ 70 = 20
   The elevator can hold 20 people at most.
9a. 12 x 12 x 4 ÷ 16 = 36
    The volume is 36 cm³.
  b. 1 kg 360 g = 1360 g
     1360 ÷ 16 = 85
     The mass of each piece is 85 g.
10. 1 kg = 1000 g
    1000 ÷ 5 = 200
    200 nickels weigh 1 kg altogether.
11a. 30 t = 30 000 kg
     $50 x 30 000 ÷ 100 = $15 000
     The yard can make $15 000.
  b. 30 000 g = 30 kg
     $50 x 30 ÷ 100 = $15
     The yard can make $15.
12. Box A: 20 x 20 x 20 = 8000
    Box B: 40 x 15 x 20 = 12 000
    Box C: 45 x 15 x 5 = 3375
    Box B has the greatest volume.
13a. 50 x 40 x 2 = 4000
     The total volume is 4000 cm³.
  b. 4000 ÷ 8 = 500
     The average volume is 500 cm³.

10 Coordinate Systems

Try It

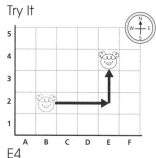

E4

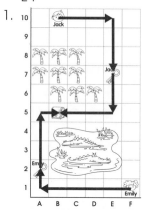

a. Move 3 blocks east and 3 blocks south.
   Move 2 blocks south and 3 blocks west.
b. Move 5 blocks west and 1 block north.
   Move 3 blocks north and 1 block east.
c. Emily has the shorter route.

2a. E2
 b. H4
 c. M3
 d. C1
 e. G3
 f. K2

3.

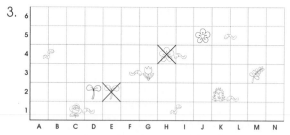

4a. It moved 3 units north and 6 units east.
 b. It moved 2 units south and 10 units west.
 c. It moved 1 unit north and 4 units west.
 d. It moved 4 units south and 7 units west.
 e. It moved 6 units east.

5.

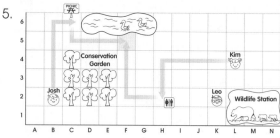

Its coordinates are F5.

6a. B2 ; 4 ; north ; 1 ; east ; 1 block south and 3 blocks east
 b. L4 ; 4 blocks west and 2 blocks south. Then she moved 2 blocks west and 3 blocks north

7. (Suggested answer)
   He should move 1 block north and 2 blocks east and then move 2 blocks north and 7 blocks west.

8a. C7 ; E6
   F4 ; H2
 b. Move 5 units south and 5 units east.
   Move 2 units north and 1 unit west.

9a. E6 ; H4 ; F8
 b. John's coordinates are F3. He should move 1 unit north and 2 units east.

11 Transformations

Try It
rotation of $\frac{1}{4}$ clockwise / $\frac{3}{4}$ counterclockwise

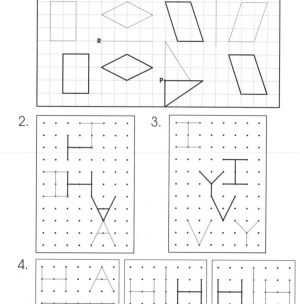

5. A

6a.

b.

7a.

b.

8.

9.

10.

11.

12. The image will not be different from the original because the "A" has a vertical line of symmetry.

12 Patterning

Try It
12

1. 7 ; 9

a. He will make 11 baskets.

b. He will make 15 baskets on Day 8.

2. 1000 ; 500

a. $\frac{1}{8}$ of 8000 is 1000.
The car will be worth $1000 in Year 4.

b. Its value will be $125 in Year 7.

3.

Day	1	2	3	4	5	6
No. of Yellow Marbles	12	14	16	18	20	22
No. of Blue Marbles	5	8	11	14	17	20

a. He has 24 yellow marbles on Day 7.

b. He has 26 blue marbles on Day 8.

c. He will have 28 yellow marbles on Day 9.

d. He will have 29 blue marbles on Day 9.

e. He will have the same number of yellow and blue marbles on Day 8.

f. 22 + 20 = 42
He has 42 marbles in all on Day 6.

4.

Dog Sitting

Time (h)	1	2	3	4	5	6
Charge ($)	4	9	14	19	24	29

Walking

Distance (km)	1	2	3	4	5	6
Charge ($)	2	4	6	8	10	12

a. The charge was $49.

b. $19 + $6 = $25
The total charge was $25.

c. $8 + $5 = $13
Her bill was $13.

d. $39 + $5 + 0 = $44
Her bill was $44.

5.

		Column				
		1	2	3	4	5	6
Row	1	2	4	6	8	10	12
	2	4	8	12	16	20	24
	3	6	12	18	24	30	36
	4	8	16	24	32	40	48
	5	10	20	30	40	50	60

a. The pattern rule is: Start at 6. Add 6 each time. The next 3 numbers are 36, 42, and 48.

b. The pattern rule is: Start at 4. Add 4 each time. The next 3 numbers are 28, 32, and 36.

c. Column 5 follows the same pattern rule as Row 5. The pattern rule is: Start at 10. Add 10 each time.

d. Row 3 shows the pattern. He will have 30 cards after 5 days.

e. Row 4 shows the total amount of money spent. He will have spent $32 after 4 days.

13 Data Analysis

Try It
B ; A

1. Discrete Data: A ; D ; E ; G
Continuous Data: B ; C ; F

2. discrete ; line

3. discrete data ; bar graph

4. continuous data ; line graph

5. discrete data ; circle graph

6. discrete data ; bar graph

7a. A: bar graph
   B: circle graph
   C: pictograph
   D: line graph
 b. 3 cards
 c. ✗
 d. 3 cars
 e. 2015 – 2016
8a. A
 b. 15 years old ; 15 years old ;14 years old
 c. A
9a. discrete data
 b. 9 toonies ; 10 toonies ; 10 toonies
 c. bar graph
10a. continuous data
 b. 3.5 mm ; 2.7 mm ; 0 mm
 c. line graph

14 Graphs (1)

Try It
A
1a. 6500 toy cars were produced in January.
 b. 6500 + 9000 + 8000 = 23 500
   23 500 toy cars were produced from January to March.
 c. 5000 – 4000 = 1000
   1000 more toy cars were produced in June than July.
 d. It shut down in December.
 e. (6500 + 9000 + 8000 + 7500 + 6000 + 5000 + 4000 + 8000 + 6000 + 8000 + 7500 + 2500) ÷ 12 = 6500
   6500 toy cars were produced each month on average.
2a. 4000 sports cars and 7000 trucks were sold in the 3rd quarter.
 b. 6000 – 2000 = 4000
   4000 more sports cars were sold in the 4th quarter than the 1st quarter.
 c. 7000 + 6000 + 7000 = 20 000
   20 000 trucks were sold from the 1st quarter to the 3rd quarter.
 d. He sold the same number of sports cars and trucks in the 4th quarter.
 e. (2000 + 3000 + 4000 + 6000) ÷ 4 = 3750
   The mean number of sports cars sold is 3750.

3a. Grade 1: 25 – 15 = 10
   The difference is 10.
   Grade 4: 30 – 10 = 20
   The difference is 20.
 b. There are more boys than girls participating in Grades 3, 4, and 5.
   There are more girls than boys participating in Grades 1, 2, and 6.
 c. Boys who participated in the activities:
   The mean is 25 boys, the median is 25 boys, and the modes are 20 and 30 boys.
   Girls who participated in the activities:
   The mean is 20 girls, the median is 20 girls, and the modes are 15 and 25 girls.
4a. B

Money Spent on Fruits

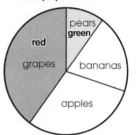

 b. The family spent the most on grape. They spent $20.
 c. The family spent the least on pears. They spent $5.
 d. $\frac{1}{10}$ of $50 is 5.
   Pears take up $\frac{1}{10}$ of the total amount spent.
 e. $\frac{15}{50} = \frac{3}{10}$
   $\frac{3}{10}$ of the total amount was spent on apples.

15 Graphs (2)

Try It
A
1. B
2. 25 – 15 = 10
   Lemon cakes were more popular than lemon muffins. 10 more lemon cakes were sold.
3. The same number of chocolate cakes and muffins were sold.
4. Cakes: 15 + 25 + 15 = 55
   Muffins: 20 + 15 + 15 = 50
   More cakes were sold.

5.

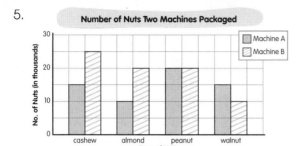

Number of Nuts Two Machines Packaged

a. 20 000 – 10 000 = 10 000

Machine B packaged more almonds by 10 000.

b. 20 000 + 20 000 = 40 000

Peanuts had the same quantity packaged by both machines. 40 000 peanuts were packaged.

c. Machine A packaged peanuts the most.

d. Machine A:

15 000 + 10 000 + 20 000 + 15 000 = 60 000

Machine B:

25 000 + 20 000 + 20 000 + 10 000 = 75 000

Yes, Machine B is more efficient because it packaged more nuts.

6.

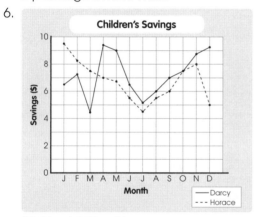

Children's Savings

a. $7.50 – $4.50 = $3

Horace had $3 more than Darcy in March.

b. $8.25 – $7.25 = $1

Horace had $1 more than Darcy in February.

c. Horace had more savings in January, February, and March.

d. Darcy's savings were more than Horace's for 8 months.

e. Their savings were the same in October.

f. ($6.50 + $7.25 + $4.50 + $9.50 + $9 + $6.50 + $5.25 + $6 + $7 + $7.50 + $8.75 + $9.25) ÷ 12 = $7.25

Darcy's mean savings was $7.25.

g. ($9.50 + $8.25 + $7.50 + $7 + $6.75 + $5.50 + $4.50 + $5.50 + $6 + $7.50 + $8 + $5) ÷ 12 = $6.75

Horace's mean savings was $6.75.

h. Darcy's savings: $7.25 x 12 = $87

Horace's savings: $6.75 x 12 = $81

Darcy had more savings in total.

7.

Stem	Leaf
1	2 5 5 9 9
2	0 1 1 3 4 5 5 5 7 7 7 8 9 9 9
3	1 1 1 2 2 4 4 4 4 5 5 8 9 9 9
4	0 0 0 2 2 2 3 7 7 8
5	0 2 3 4 4

Apples Sold by 50 Scouts

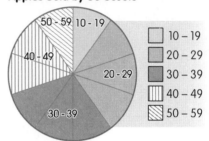

a. The 40 – 49 range accounts for $\frac{1}{5}$ of the number of apples sold.

b. The 30 – 39 range takes up the same amount of space as the 20 – 29 range.

c. The 20 – 29 and 30 – 39 ranges take up more than half of the circle graph.

d. She is in the 40 – 49 range.

16 Probability

Try It

$\frac{5}{12}$

1a. The probability is $\frac{5}{8}$.

b. The probability is $\frac{2}{5}$.

c. The probability is $\frac{4}{9}$.

d. Emily said this.

e. Emily: 0

Peter: $\frac{4}{10} = \frac{36}{90}$

Doris: $\frac{4}{9} = \frac{40}{90}$ ← greatest

Doris has the greatest chance of picking a blue marble.

2a. The probability is $\frac{1}{4}$.

  b. The probability is $\frac{1}{3}$.

  c. The probability is $\frac{1}{8}$.

  d. Spinner C has the greatest probability of landing on "Hot Dog". The probability is $\frac{3}{8}$.

  e. Spinner C has the smallest probability of landing on "Try Again Next Time". The probability is $\frac{1}{8}$.

  f. He should choose Spinner C. The probability of landing on either prize is $\frac{5}{8}$.

3a. No. of Students: $2 + 10 + 1 + 7 = 20$

$$\frac{2}{20} = \frac{1}{10}$$

The probability is $\frac{1}{10}$.

  b. The probability is $\frac{7}{20}$.

4. No. of girls: $1 + 7 = 8$

$$\frac{8}{20} = \frac{2}{5}$$

The probability is $\frac{2}{5}$.

5.

```
        R ——— H, R
H <     Y ——— H, Y
        B ——— H, B

        R ——— T, R
T <     Y ——— T, Y
        B ——— T, B
```

  a. There are 6 possible outcomes.

  b. The probability is $\frac{1}{6}$.

  c. Yes, all the possible outcomes are equally likely because flipping a coin and taking a marble from the bag are both fair games. Also, the probability of getting each possible outcome is the same, which is $\frac{1}{6}$.

ASSESSMENT TESTS 1 AND 2

Test-taking Tips

Writing tests can be stressful for many students. The best way to prepare for a test is by practising! In addition to practising, the test-taking tips below will also help you prepare for tests.

Multiple-choice Questions

- Read the question twice before finding the answer.
- Skip the difficult questions and do the easy ones first.
- Come up with an answer before looking at the choices.
- Read all four choices before deciding which is the correct answer.
- Eliminate the choices that you know are incorrect.
- Read and follow the instructions carefully:
  - Use a pencil only.
  - Fill one circle only for each question.
  - Fill the circle completely.
  - Cleanly erase any answer you wish to change.

    e.g.

    correct　　　　　　incorrect

Open-response Questions

- Read the question carefully.
- Highlight (i.e. underline/circle) important information in the question.
- Use drawings to help you better understand the question if needed.
- Find out what needs to be included in the solution.
- Estimate the answer.
- Organize your thoughts before writing the solution.
- Write in the space provided.
- Always write a concluding sentence for your solution.
- Check if your answer is reasonable.
- Never leave a question blank. Show your work or write down your reasoning. Even if you do not get the correct answer, you might get some marks for showing your work.

Multiple-choice Questions

> You may not use a calculator or manipulatives for Questions 1 – 4.

① What is the answer?

4206 + 1957 − 2514

- ○ 3265
- ○ 3649
- ○ 4763
- ○ 7677

② Which multiplication question has the greatest product?

- ○ 88 x 39
- ○ 67 x 51
- ○ 74 x 47
- ○ 55 x 62

③ What are the missing numbers in order?

$3.9 \div \boxed{} = 0.39$

$195 \div 1000 = \boxed{}$

$\boxed{} \div 100 = 0.041$

- ○ 100, 0.195, 41
- ○ 10, 0.195, 4.1
- ○ 1000, 19.5, 0.41
- ○ 10, 0.0195, 4.1

④ What is the difference in mass?

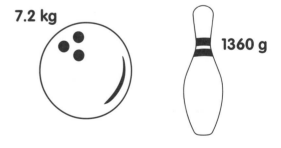

7.2 kg

1360 g

- ○ 5840 g
- ○ 8560 g
- ○ 6.4 kg
- ○ 7.064 kg

You may now use a calculator and/or manipulatives.

⑤ Which fraction describes the shaded part?

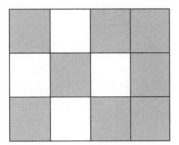

- ○ $\dfrac{5}{6}$
- ○ $\dfrac{4}{5}$
- ○ $\dfrac{2}{3}$
- ○ $\dfrac{5}{12}$

⑥ Which fraction is not equivalent to the others?

- ○ $\dfrac{11}{5}$
- ○ $1\dfrac{9}{15}$
- ○ $1\dfrac{6}{10}$
- ○ $\dfrac{32}{20}$

⑦ Look at the thermometer below.

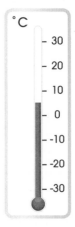

What will the temperature be if it drops by 15°C?

- ○ 15°C
- ○ 5°C
- ○ 10° below 0°C
- ○ 20° below 0°C

⑧ How much money is there?

- ○ $138.30
- ○ $154.75
- ○ $162.30
- ○ $211.10

⑨ What is the probability of spinning red?

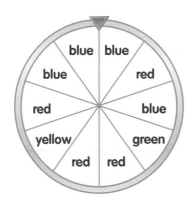

- ○ $\frac{1}{10}$
- ○ $\frac{2}{5}$
- ○ $\frac{1}{2}$
- ○ $\frac{3}{10}$

⑩ What is the volume of the rectangular prism?

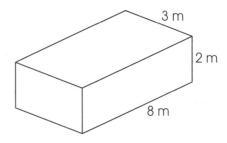

- ○ 32 m³
- ○ 48 m³
- ○ 52 m³
- ○ 78 m³

⑪ Name the triangle by its angles and by its sides.

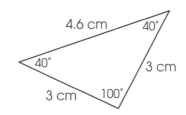

- ○ acute triangle; isosceles triangle
- ○ right triangle; scalene triangle
- ○ obtuse triangle; equilateral triangle
- ○ obtuse triangle; isosceles triangle

⑫ Lucy folds the net into a solid. How many vertices does it have?

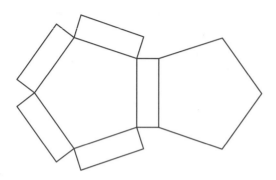

- ○ 10
- ○ 11
- ○ 18
- ○ 21

⑬ Look at the grid below.

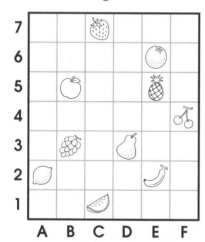

Which of the following squares on the grid is empty?

- ○ B5
- ○ E4
- ○ D3
- ○ C7

⑭ What are the mean, median, and mode of the data set?

270	170	260	240
250	200	270	200
290	150	260	200

- ○ Mean: 220
  Median: 240
  Mode: 270

- ○ Mean: 250
  Median: 245
  Mode: 260

- ○ Mean: 200
  Median: 230
  Mode: 245

- ○ Mean: 230
  Median: 245
  Mode: 200

⑮ What is the area of the square?

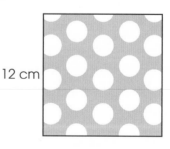

12 cm

- ○ 112 cm²
- ○ 120 cm²
- ○ 144 cm²
- ○ 192 cm²

Open-response Questions

⑯ Wendy recorded her babysitting earnings in the table. Help her complete the line graph.

Wendy's Babysitting Earnings Over 9 Months

Month	Earnings ($)
Jan	130
Feb	220
Mar	240
Apr	200
May	140
Jun	120
Jul	90
Aug	210
Sep	280

She says, "My babysitting earnings had the greatest increase in August and the greatest decrease in July." Is she correct? If not, find the correct months.

⑰ Jackie first placed a rock in a measuring cup. Then she moved the rock into an aquarium as shown. The water level changes are shaded. Can the capacity of the aquarium be found? If so, what is it?

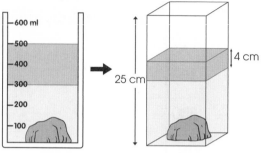

⑱ A box contains 9 balls. Use the descriptions to label the balls. Then find the probabilities of all the outcomes if one ball is picked at a time.

- There are 4 possible outcomes: red (R), blue (B), yellow (Y), and green (G).

- It is equally likely to pick blue or yellow.

- Picking red is four times as likely as picking green.

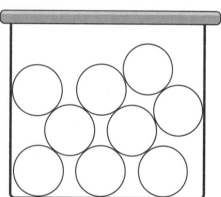

Multiple-choice Questions

You may not use a calculator or manipulatives for Questions 1 – 4.

① Which division sentence is incorrect?

    ○ 452 ÷ 3 = 150R2

    ○ 513 ÷ 5 = 102R3

    ○ 608 ÷ 4 = 152R2

    ○ 781 ÷ 6 = 130R1

② What is the answer?

    4.98 – 1.77 + 2.64

    ○ 0.57

    ○ 4.11

    ○ 5.85

    ○ 9.39

③ Which multiplication question has an answer of 1450?

    ○ 14.5 x 5 x 2

    ○ 250 x 4 x 0.145

    ○ 125 x 1.45 x 8

    ○ 0.0145 x 5 x 20

④ How much change will you get if you pay for the meal with a $50 bill?

$4.37

$6.28

$18.99

    ○ $20.36

    ○ $23.36

    ○ $24.73

    ○ $29.64

> **You may now use a calculator and/or manipulatives.**

⑤ Which set of fractions is in the correct order?

○ $\frac{5}{4} < \frac{3}{4} < 1\frac{1}{4}$

○ $2\frac{1}{6} > \frac{11}{6} > 1\frac{1}{6}$

○ $\frac{9}{5} < \frac{13}{5} < 2\frac{2}{5}$

○ $\frac{11}{8} > \frac{13}{8} > 1\frac{7}{8}$

⑥ Which is the missing number?

$$0.65 > ? > \frac{11}{20}$$

○ 0.45

○ 0.52

○ $\frac{3}{5}$

○ $\frac{7}{10}$

⑦ Which clock shows 20:45:30?

○

○

○

○

⑧ Which is the correct way to make $83.60 using the fewest bills and coins?

○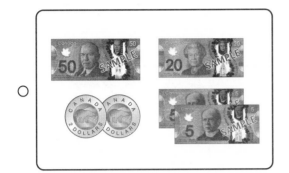

○

○

○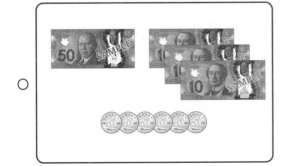

⑨ Which conversion is correct?

○ 15 g = 1500 mg

○ 4500 mm = 450 cm

○ 20 000 kg = 2 t

○ 600 m = 6 km

⑩ What is the area of the rectangle?

1.5 cm

4 mm

○ 0.6 mm²

○ 6 cm²

○ 60 mm²

○ 60 cm²

⑪ Which shape has the following properties?

- all equal sides
- more than 2 lines of symmetry
- 4 vertices

○ rhombus

○ square

○ parallelogram

○ pentagon

⑫ Which solid has the same number of faces and vertices and more than 6 edges?

○

○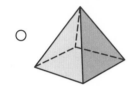

○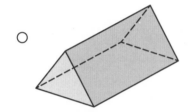

○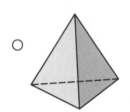

⑬ What is the pattern rule?

3, 10, 24, 52, 108

○ Start at 3. Add 7 and divide by 2 alternately.

○ Start at 3. Multiply by 4 and subtract 2 each time.

○ Start at 3. Multiply by 3 and add 1 each time.

○ Start at 3. Add 2 and multiply by 2 each time.

⑭ Which statement describes the transformation incorrectly?

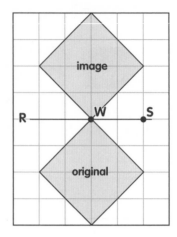

○ translation of 4 units up

○ reflection in Line R

○ $\frac{1}{4}$ turn counterclockwise about Point S

○ $\frac{1}{2}$ turn about Point W

⑮ The a in which equation has a value of 6?

○ $30 \div a = 6$

○ $4 \times a = 24$

○ $a + 5 = 12$

○ $a - 2 = 5$

Open-response Questions

⑯ Daniel collected candy in his neighbourhood. He started at G3 and moved 5 blocks north, 3 blocks west, and 2 blocks south. He then reached C2 by moving west and then south.

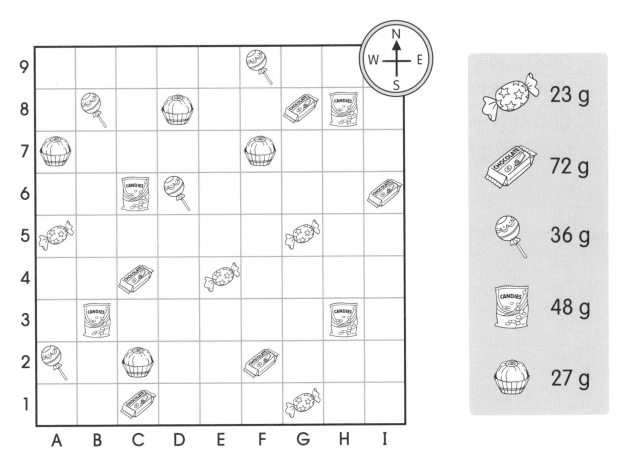

Draw Daniel's route.

Daniel moved one more square to get his last piece of candy. What was his final location? Did he collect more than 1 kg of candy in total?

⑰ Prima has 5 cards in different colours as shown. She creates a game by putting the cards into 2 piles. One card is drawn from each pile each round. She says, "The probability of drawing a red card is $\frac{1}{2}$ and a blue card $\frac{1}{3}$, while the probability of drawing both a blue card and a green card is $\frac{1}{6}$." Draw a tree diagram to show all the possible outcomes and find how the cards were put into 2 piles.

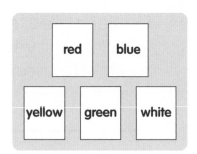

⑱ The circle graph shows the hourly wages of 20 students. What is the mean wage of the students?

(Hint: find how many students earn each wage first.)

Hourly Wages of 20 Students

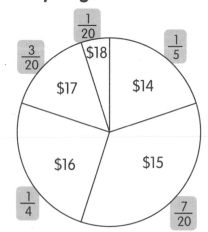

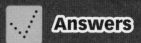

Assessment Test 1

1. 3649
2. 74 x 47
3. 10, 0.195, 4.1
4. 5840 g
5. $\frac{2}{3}$
6. $\frac{11}{5}$
7. 10° below 0°C
8. $138.30
9. $\frac{2}{5}$
10. 48 m³
11. obtuse triangle;
    isosceles triangle
12. 10
13. E4
14. Mean: 230
    Median: 245
    Mode: 200
15. 144 cm²
16.

No, she is not correct. While August did have the greatest increase, the greatest decrease occurred in May.

17. Yes, the capacity of the aquarium can be found.
    Volume of the rock:
    500 – 300 = 200 (mL) = 200 (cm³)
    Base area of aquarium: 200 ÷ 4 = 50 (cm²)
    Capacity of aquarium:
    50 x 25 = 1250 (cm³) = 1250 (mL)
    The capacity of the aquarium is 1250 mL.

18.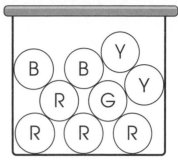

The probability of picking a red ball is $\frac{4}{9}$, blue is $\frac{2}{9}$, yellow is $\frac{2}{9}$, and green is $\frac{1}{9}$.

Assessment Test 2

1. $608 \div 4 = 152R2$
2. 5.85
3. $125 \times 1.45 \times 8$
4. $\$20.36$
5. $2\frac{1}{6} > \frac{11}{6} > 1\frac{1}{6}$
6. $\frac{3}{5}$
7.

8.

9. 4500 mm $= 450$ cm
10. 60 mm²
11. square
12.

13. Start at 3. Add 2 and multiply by 2 each time.
14. $\frac{1}{4}$ turn counterclockwise about Point S
15. $4 \times a = 24$

16.

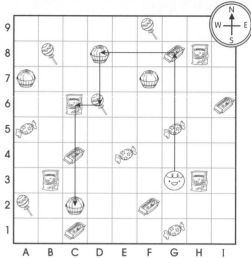

His final location was C1.

$23 + 72 + 27 + 36 + 48 + 72 + 27 + 72$
$= 377$ (g)
$= 0.377$ (kg)

No, he did not collect more than 1 kg of candy in total.

17.

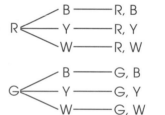

The 2 piles are a pile with the red and green cards and a pile with the blue, yellow, and white cards.

18. $\$14$: $\frac{1}{5} = \frac{4}{20}$ ➡ 4 students

$\$15$: $\frac{7}{20}$ ➡ 7 students

$\$16$: $\frac{1}{4} = \frac{5}{20}$ ➡ 5 students

$\$17$: $\frac{3}{20}$ ➡ 3 students

$\$18$: $\frac{1}{20}$ ➡ 1 student

Mean wage: ($\$14 \times 4 + \$15 \times 7 + \$16 \times 5 + \$17 \times 3 + \$18 \times 1) \div 20 = \$15.50$

The mean wage is $\$15.50$.